# MATHS

## FOR PRACTICE & REVISION

MATRICES

VECTORS

SIMULTANEOUS AND
QUADRATIC EQUATIONS

TRIGONOMETRY

CIRCLES

## PETER ROBSON

 **Newby Books**

PO BOX 40, SCARBOROUGH
NORTH YORKSHIRE, YO12 5TW
TEL/FAX 01723 362713
www.newbybooks.co.uk

# A SQUARE ROOTS

## Finding the square root (√) of a number

If a number is not a perfect square (integer X itself) the square root will not work out exactly.

Square roots to an accuracy of 3 significant figures can be worked out using the table in the back of this book.
For greater accuracy, use an electronic calculator with a √ button.

The examples on this page are worked out to 3 significant figures.

e.g. (1) Calculate the square root of 5000

*If the number is between 1 and 100 (inclusive), simply look up in the table. Otherwise, change the number by dividing or multiplying <u>by 100</u> until you have a new number between 1 and 100

$5000 \div 100 = 50$

*Look up the square root of your new number     $\sqrt{50} = 7.07$

*Multiply or divide your square root <u>by 10</u> the correct number of times

$7.07 \times 10 = 70.7$

Answer $\sqrt{5000} = 70.7$

---

e.g. (2) Find the value of $\sqrt{83000}$

$83000 \div 100 \div 100 = 8.3$
$\sqrt{8.3} = 2.88$
$\sqrt{83000} = 2.88 \times 10 \times 10 = 288$

---

e.g. (3) Find the square root of 0.09

$0.09 \times 100 = 9$
$\sqrt{9} = 3$
$\sqrt{0.09} = 3 \div 10 = 0.3$

---

e.g. (4) Find, to 3 sig. figs., the square root of 0.0059

$0.0059 \times 100 \times 100 = 59$

$\sqrt{59} = 7.68$
$\sqrt{0.0059} = 7.68 \div 10 \div 10$
$= 0.0768$

---

**NOTE** Square roots can be worked out by trial and error (even on a desert island without a calculator) if you remember some rough guidelines: $\sqrt{1} = 1$, $\sqrt{4} = 2$, $\sqrt{9} = 3$, $\sqrt{16} = 4$, $\sqrt{25} = 5$, $\sqrt{36} = 6$, $\sqrt{49} = 7$, etc., e.g. $\sqrt{38}$ must be between 6 and 7, so try 6.1 x 6.1, etc.

**a** Look up, in the table on page 71, the square roots of these numbers

| | | | | |
|---|---|---|---|---|
| 1) 17 | 4) 41 | 7) 1.3 | 10) 67 | 13) 50 |
| 2) 75 | 5) 5.9 | 8) 9.0 | 11) 6.7 | 14) 5.0 |
| 3) 3.4 | 6) 86 | 9) 22 | 12) 15 | 15) 7.7 |

**b** Find the square root of each of these numbers

| | | |
|---|---|---|
| 1) 230 | 6) 1400 | 11) 18000 |
| 2) 8300 | 7) 0.69 | 12) 35 |
| 3) 57000 | 8) 650 | 13) 0.42 |
| 4) 2.8 | 9) 0.088 | 14) 7100 |
| 5) 0.028 | 10) 0.0088 | 15) 0.054 |

**c** Find the value of each of these

| | | |
|---|---|---|
| 1) $\sqrt{0.33}$ . | 6) $\sqrt{1000}$ | 11) $\sqrt{0.085}$ |
| 2) $\sqrt{68}$ | 7) $\sqrt{1.8}$ | 12) $\sqrt{620}$ |
| 3) $\sqrt{45000}$ | 8) $\sqrt{0.0052}$ | 13) $\sqrt{0.00023}$ |
| 4) $\sqrt{0.092}$ | 9) $\sqrt{490}$ | 14) $\sqrt{1900000}$ |
| 5) $\sqrt{390000}$ | 10) $\sqrt{4900}$ | 15) $\sqrt{0.74}$ |

**d** Using the table on page 71, estimate the square root of each of these numbers

| | | |
|---|---|---|
| 1) 78.5 | 6) 3.35 | 11) 11.5 |
| 2) 26.5 | 7) 63.5 | 12) 4.45 |
| 3) 2.05 | 8) 9.25 | 13) 46.5 |
| 4) 82.5 | 9) 1.35 | 14) 6.85 |
| 5) 7.75 | 10) 55.5 | 15) 1.25 |

**e** Find the **square** of each of these numbers

1) 15     2) 41     3) 24     4) 9     5) 67

From your answers to questions 1, 2, 3, 4 and 5 (but not in that order), write down the exact square root of

| | | |
|---|---|---|
| 6) 8100 | 8) 448900 | 10) 0.0576 |
| 7) 16.81 | 9) 2.25 | |

# A PYTHAGORAS' THEOREM

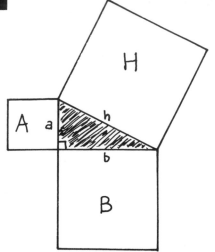

In a right-angled triangle, the square on the hypotenuse is equal to the sum of the squares on the other two sides.

NOTE. The hypotenuse is the longest side of a right-angled triangle (i.e. the side opposite the right angle)

In the diagram
area H = area A + area B
or $h^2 = a^2 + b^2$

e.g. (1) Find the length of h if a = 3cm, b = 4cm

$$h^2 = 3^2 + 4^2$$
$$h^2 = 9 + 16$$
$$h^2 = 25$$
$$h = \sqrt{25}$$
$$h = 5 \qquad \text{Length of h is 5cm}$$

e.g. (2) Find the length, correct to 1 decimal place, of the hypotenuse of a triangle whose other two sides are 11cm and 19cm

$$h^2 = 11^2 + 19^2$$
$$h^2 = 121 + 361$$
$$h^2 = 482$$
$$h = \sqrt{482}$$
$$h = 22.0 \text{ cm (1 d.p.)}$$

e.g. (3) Find the length b, correct to 1 decimal place, if h = 23m and a = 20m

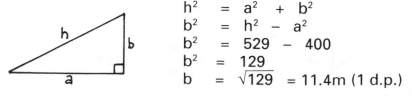

$$h^2 = a^2 + b^2$$
$$b^2 = h^2 - a^2$$
$$b^2 = 529 - 400$$
$$b^2 = 129$$
$$b = \sqrt{129} = 11.4\text{m (1 d.p.)}$$

**a** Find the length of the hypotenuse (h) in each triangle. If the square root does not work out exactly (questions 11 to 20) give your answer correct to 1 decimal place

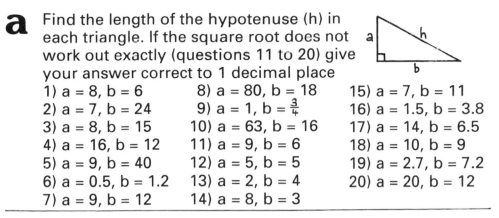

1) a = 8, b = 6
2) a = 7, b = 24
3) a = 8, b = 15
4) a = 16, b = 12
5) a = 9, b = 40
6) a = 0.5, b = 1.2
7) a = 9, b = 12

8) a = 80, b = 18
9) a = 1, b = $\frac{3}{4}$
10) a = 63, b = 16
11) a = 9, b = 6
12) a = 5, b = 5
13) a = 2, b = 4
14) a = 8, b = 3

15) a = 7, b = 11
16) a = 1.5, b = 3.8
17) a = 14, b = 6.5
18) a = 10, b = 9
19) a = 2.7, b = 7.2
20) a = 20, b = 12

**b** Find the length of a in each triangle (like the one at the top of the page). If the square root does not work out exactly (questions 11 to 15) give your answer correct to 1 decimal place.

1) h = 26, b = 10
2) h = 61, b = 60
3) h = 25, b = 20
4) h = 7.5, b = 2.1
5) h = 39, b = 36

6) h = $2\frac{1}{6}$ , b = $\frac{5}{6}$
7) b = 80, h = 100
8) h = 221, b = 21
9) h = 0.05, b = 0.04
10) b = 30, h = 34

11) h = 10, b = 5
12) h = 43, b = 27
13) h = 6, b = 4.5
14) b = 19, h = 22
15) h = 3.4, b = 0.8

**c** 1) Tebsworth is 9 miles due north of Petersby; Dalton is 12 miles due east of Petersby. How far is Tebsworth from Dalton?

2) A ladder is placed with its foot on level ground 4 m from a vertical wall. The top of the ladder is 7.5 m up the wall. Find the length of the ladder.

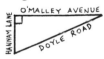

3) In the drawing on the left, Doyle Road is 650 m long and O'Malley Avenue is 630 m long. How long is Hannam Lane?

4) In the drawing on the right, a vertical flagpole (TB) 10 m high is secured by a wire (TW) 12.5 m long. How far is the bottom of the wire from the foot of the flagpole?

5)

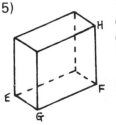

The drawing shows a box in the shape of a cuboid 48 cm long (GF), 36 cm wide (EG), 25 cm high (FH).
(a) By studying triangle EFG, work out the length EF
(b) From your answer to part (a) and by studying triangle EFH, work out the length EH

# 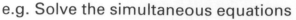 A SIMULTANEOUS EQUATIONS(1)

To solve simultaneous equations, the values of two (or more) different letters must be found.

e.g. Solve the simultaneous equations

$$x + y = 8 \qquad \text{Answer} \quad \begin{cases} x = 5 \\ y = 3 \end{cases}$$
$$x - y = 2$$

because $5 + 3 = 8$

$5 - 3 = 2$

The answer to simultaneous equations is written with a curly bracket

$$\begin{cases} x = \\ y = \end{cases}$$

There are several different ways of solving simultaneous equations, including

        1) substitution
        2) elimination (see page 8 [A])
        3) drawing graphs (see page 10 [A])
        4) using matrices (see page 20 [C])

---

# B Substitution

e.g. Solve the simultaneous equations

$$x + y = 12$$
$$2x - y = 9$$

$$x + y = 12 \ \text{....equation} \ ①$$
$$2x - y = 9 \ \text{....equation} \ ②$$

*Rearrange equation ① to give the value of y in terms of x

$$y = 12 - x$$

*Now, using this value of y, substitute for y in equation ②

$$2x - (12 - x) = 9$$

*Solve for x

$$2x - 12 + x = 9$$
$$3x = 21$$
$$x = 7$$

*Find the value of y by substituting in equation ①

$7 + y = 12$, so the answer is

$$\begin{cases} x = 7 \\ y = 5 \end{cases}$$

*NOTE. For the first stage, always choose the easier of the two equations. It does not matter which letter value is found first.

**a** Solve these simultaneous equations by substitution

1) $x + y = 10$
   $x - y = 6$

2) $a + b = 7$
   $2a - b = 5$

3) $3j + h = 29$
   $j - h = 3$

4) $m + 2p = 17$
   $m + p = 12$

5) $x - y = 1$
   $3y - 2x = 8$

6) $d + e = 13$
   $2d - 4e = 20$

7) $4q + p = 13$
   $p - q = 3$

8) $2d - c = 8$
   $c - d = 1$

9) $2v + w = 7$
   $2w + v = 8$

10) $3a - c = 3$
    $c - a = 5$

11) $k - m = 2$
    $3m - k = 6$

12) $2x + y = 5$
    $x - y = 1$

13) $2t - s = 12$
    $2s + t = 6$

14) $g - e = -1$
    $e + g = 5$

15) $a - 3k = -5$
    $k - a = -3$

**b** Solve these simultaneous equations

1) $w + 3u = 2$
   $u - w = 6$

2) $x + y = 3$
   $x - y = 9$

3) $m + 2j = 3$
   $j + 2m = 9$

4) $e - d = 2$
   $2d - e = 2$

5) $z + y = 6$
   $2z - y = 18$

6) $t - u = 2$
   $3t + u = 2$

7) $4b - 2a = -6$
   $a - b = 1$

8) $3f - g = 12$
   $f + 3g = -6$

9) $p - q = -1$
   $2q - p = 6$

10) $x + y = -7$
    $5y - 4x = 1$

11) $4c + d = 4$
    $d - 2c = 1$

12) $m + 5n = 4$
    $2n - 6m = 8$

13) $4x - y = 6$
    $y + 2x = 9$

14) $2q - 3s = -14$
    $q - s = 2$

15) $2h + t = 2$
    $2t + 6h = 1$

**c** Solve for x and y in each of these by substitution

1) $y = x + 2$
   $3x + 1 = 2y$

2) $y = 2x + 6$
   $x + y = 3$

3) $x - 3y = 2$
   $y = \frac{1}{4}x + 2$

4) $y = 2x - 5$
   $3y + 4x = 20$

5) $y + 4x = -6$
   $3x + 7y = 8$

6) $12x + y = -1$
   $4x - 2y = 16$

7) $x = 2y - 1$
   $3y - 2x + 6 = 0$

8) $x + 10y = 1$
   $8y + 2x = 8$

9) $y = \frac{1}{4}x + 3$
   $x + 8y = 18$

10) $x = y + 9$
    $3x + y = 7$

# A SIMULTANEOUS EQUATIONS(2)

## Elimination

This is done by making sure first that both equations have a matching letter-term ( e.g. x, y, 2x, 3y, 5x, etc). Depending on the signs of the matching terms, the equations are either <u>added</u> or <u>subtracted</u> to eliminate (get rid of) one of the letters.

e.g. Solve the simultaneous equations

$$3x + 2y = 19 \qquad ....\text{equation} \textcircled{1}$$
$$x - 2y = 1 \qquad ....\text{equation} \textcircled{2}$$

Both equations have a 2y term. The signs are unlike (+ −).

If equations ① and ② are added, the y terms are eliminated

$$3x + 2y = 19 \ ... \ \textcircled{1}$$
$$\underline{x - 2y = 1 \ ... \ \textcircled{2}}$$
$$4x \qquad = 20 \ \text{so} \ x = 5$$

Now substitute in either equation (whichever is simpler),

e.g. substitute in equation ①

$$15 + 2y = 19 \qquad \text{so} \ y = 2 \qquad \begin{cases} x = 5 \\ y = 2 \end{cases}$$

---

e.g. (2) Solve $3x + 4y = 15 \qquad .... \ \textcircled{1}$

$$3x - 3y = -6 \qquad .... \ \textcircled{2}$$

Both equations have a 3x term. The signs are like (+ +).

If ② is subtracted from ①, the x terms are eliminated

$$7y = 21 \ , \qquad \text{so} \ y = 3 \qquad \begin{cases} x = 1 \\ y = 3 \end{cases}$$

Substituting in either equation, x = 1

---

e.g. (3) Solve $4x - 2y = 10 \qquad .... \ \textcircled{1}$

$$3x + y = 15 \qquad .... \textcircled{2}$$

No terms are similar, so MULTIPLY all through one (or both) of the equations to give similar terms

Multiply ② by 2 $\qquad 6x + 2y = 30 \ .... \ \textcircled{3}$

$$4x - 2y = 10 \ .... \ \textcircled{1}$$

Signs are unlike, so add ③ and ①

$$10x \quad = 40, \qquad \text{so} \ x = 4 \qquad \begin{cases} x = 4 \\ y = 3 \end{cases}$$

Substituting in either equation, y = 3

---

If terms are arranged unsuitably in the question, rearrange them so that x is beneath x, y is beneath y, etc. Be careful to change signs of terms where necessary.

## a Solve by adding the equations

1) $a + b = 12$
   $a - b = 2$

2) $3r - t = 1$
   $2r + t = 9$

3) $2x + y = 18$
   $4x - y = 24$

4) $2k + m = 7$
   $4k - m = 8$

5) $d + 2h = 22$
   $3d - 2h = 26$

6) $a + b = 3$
   $a - b = 5$

7) $2x - y = -10$
   $x + y = 1$

8) $3m + 2n = 25$
   $4m - 2n = 10$

9) $4j - k = 12$
   $3j + k = 9$

10) $2p + 6q = 0$
    $p - 6q = 18$

## b Solve by subtracting one equation from the other

1) $5x + y = 22$
   $3x + y = 14$

2) $6p - q = 13$
   $2p - q = 1$

3) $j + 7k = 53$
   $j + 4k = 35$

4) $3e + d = 8$
   $2e + d = 8$

5) $3v + t = 26$
   $3v - 4t = 1$

6) $4x - 2y = 6$
   $x - 2y = 0$

7) $3b + a = 7$
   $b + a = 1$

8) $4h + 7m = 4$
   $4h - 4m = 48$

9) $3s - 5w = 0$
   $s - 5w = -10$

10) $2n - p = 7$
    $2n + 2p = 4$

## c Solve these simultaneous equations

1) $2x + y = 7$
   $4x - y = 5$

2) $2x + 3y = 15$
   $2x + y = 7$

3) $x + 3y = 23$
   $2x - y = 4$

4) $3x + 5y = 4$
   $x + y = 0$

5) $x + 2y = 8$
   $3x - 3y = 15$

6) $4x - 3y = 2$
   $x + 2y = -5$

7) $2x - 3y = -1$
   $3x - 2y = 6$

8) $4x + y = 7$
   $x + 2y = 14$

9) $2x + 5y = 0$
   $4x - y = 11$

10) $5x + y = 13$
    $2x - y = 8$

11) $2x + y = 20$
    $x + 4y = 10$

12) $3x - 8y = 2$
    $2x + 4y = 6$

13) $2x + 3y = 11$
    $5x + 2y = 11$

14) $2x + 3y = -7$
    $4x - 2y = 10$

15) $x - 3y = 0$
    $y - 3x = 16$

16) $3x + 2y = 123$
    $4x = 3y + 28$

17) $3x - 4y = 6$
    $y - 5x = 7$

18) $x - 6y = 4$
    $3x - 7y = 1$

19) $4y - 2x = 12$
    $3x - 2y = 2$

20) $y - 2x = 9$
    $2y + 8x = 12$

# A SIMULTANEOUS EQUATIONS(3)

**Graphical method** (By drawing graphs)
Simultaneous equations can sometimes be solved quite easily by drawing the graph of each equation on squared or graph paper. The intersection of the graphs is the solution of the equations.

e.g. Solve these simultaneous equations by drawing graphs

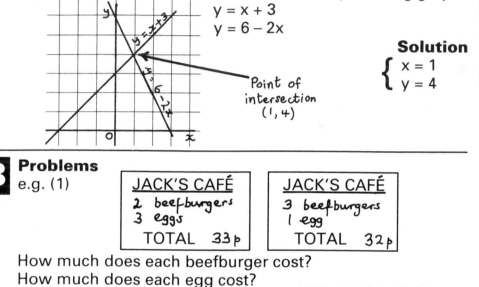

$y = x + 3$
$y = 6 - 2x$

**Solution**
$$\begin{cases} x = 1 \\ y = 4 \end{cases}$$

Point of
intersection
(1, 4)

# B Problems

e.g. (1)

| JACK'S CAFÉ |
| --- |
| 2 beefburgers |
| 3 eggs |
| TOTAL 33p |

| JACK'S CAFÉ |
| --- |
| 3 beefburgers |
| 1 egg |
| TOTAL 32p |

How much does each beefburger cost?
How much does each egg cost?

$$2b + 3e = 33$$
$$3b + e = 32$$

By either substitution (page 6) or elimination (page 8),

$$\begin{cases} b = 9 \\ e = 5 \end{cases}$$  Each beefburger costs 9p
Each egg costs 5p

e.g. (2) Aunt Peg has in her purse x 50p coins, y 20p coins and no other coins. Altogether she has 13 coins and their total is £4.10.

(a) How many 50p coins are there?
(b) How many 20p coins are there?

Equation for number of coins    $x + y = 13$
Equation for amount of money    $50x + 20y = 410$
By substitution or elimination

$$\begin{cases} x = 5 \\ y = 8 \end{cases}$$  There are 5    50p coins
There are 8    20p coins

**a** Solve these simultaneous equations by drawing graphs. Use squared paper or graph paper

1) $y = x + 2$
 $y = 5 - 2x$

2) $y = 3x - 2$
 $x + y = -6$

3) $y = \frac{1}{2}x - 1$
 $y = x - 4$

4) $y = 4x + 1$
 $y = 2x + 2$

5) $x + y = 1$
 $y = 2x + 4$

6) $y = 4 - 3x$
 $y = 2x - 1$

7) $y = x$
 $y = 4x + 6$

8) $y = x + 1$
 $2x + y = 4$

9) $y = 2x + 3$
 $y + x = -6$

10) $y = 8 - x$
 $y = x - 2$

**b** Write these problems as simultaneous equations and find the answers.

1) 12 toffees and 4 mints cost 44p; 7 toffees and 5 mints cost 31p. How much does each toffee cost?

2) Jamie spent 86p on 2 cans of orange drink and 3 packets of crisps; Carla spent 80p on 3 cans of orange and 1 packet of crisps. Find the cost of (i) a can of orange, (ii) a packet of crisps.

3) The sum of Christine's and Fiona's ages is 23 and the difference between their ages is 5. Christine is the older girl. How old is she?

4) Two footballs and six tennis balls cost £16; three footballs and five tennis balls cost £22. Find how much a football costs.

5) 3 similar buckets and 5 similar jugs hold 32 litres altogether; 2 buckets and 12 jugs hold 30 litres altogether. How many litres does each bucket hold?

6) The sum of two whole numbers x and y is 63. The difference between the same two numbers is 35. What are the two numbers?

7) The Smith family (2 adults and 3 children) went by train to the seaside. Their tickets cost £24 altogether. The Green family (3 adults and 4 children) went on the same journey and it cost them £34. How much was (i) an adult ticket? (ii) a child's ticket?

8) John has x 10p coins and y 5p coins. Altogether he has 31 coins and their total value is £2.40. Find how many 10p coins he has.

9) Four large boxes and three small boxes piled one on top of another reach a height of 168cm. Three large boxes and four small boxes reach a height of 154cm. How high is a small box?

10) Mohinder buys 2 fritters and a bag of chips for £1.25. Dalip buys 3 fritters and 2 bags of chips for £2.05. Ranjid buys 1 fritter and 3 bags of chips. How much does he pay?

# A MATRICES (1)

A MATRIX is an arrangement of numbers in rows and/or columns within brackets. If there are more than one, they are called MATRICES (pronounced may-tree-seez).

### Addition
Each matrix in addition and subtraction must have the same pattern of numbers. Add the number in the first matrix to the number <u>in the same position</u> in the other matrix (or matrices).

e.g. (1) $(2 \quad 3) + (5 \quad 1) = (2 + 5 \quad 3 + 1) = (7 \quad 4)$

e.g. (2) $\begin{pmatrix} 4 \\ 2 \end{pmatrix} + \begin{pmatrix} 6 \\ 5 \end{pmatrix} + \begin{pmatrix} 1 \\ 6 \end{pmatrix} = \begin{pmatrix} 4 + 6 + 1 \\ 2 + 5 + 6 \end{pmatrix} = \begin{pmatrix} 11 \\ 13 \end{pmatrix}$

e.g. (3) $\begin{pmatrix} 5 & 1 \\ 0 & 6 \end{pmatrix} + \begin{pmatrix} 2 & 7 \\ 3 & 3 \end{pmatrix} = \begin{pmatrix} 5 + 2 & 1 + 7 \\ 0 + 3 & 6 + 3 \end{pmatrix} = \begin{pmatrix} 7 & 8 \\ 3 & 9 \end{pmatrix}$

Be careful with negative numbers

e.g. (4) $\begin{pmatrix} 8 & -1 \\ 2 & 3 \end{pmatrix} + \begin{pmatrix} 0 & 6 \\ -5 & 2 \end{pmatrix} = \begin{pmatrix} 8 + 0 & -1 + 6 \\ 2 + -5 & 3 + 2 \end{pmatrix} = \begin{pmatrix} 8 & 5 \\ -3 & 5 \end{pmatrix}$

# B Subtraction
Subtract the number in the second matrix from the number in the same position in the first matrix

e.g. (1) $(12 \quad 7) - (4 \quad 5) = (12 - 4 \quad 7 - 5) = (8 \quad 2)$

e.g. (2) $\begin{pmatrix} 5 \\ 2 \\ 9 \end{pmatrix} - \begin{pmatrix} 1 \\ 5 \\ 2 \end{pmatrix} = \begin{pmatrix} 5 - 1 \\ 2 - 5 \\ 9 - 2 \end{pmatrix} = \begin{pmatrix} 4 \\ -3 \\ 7 \end{pmatrix}$

e.g. (3) $\begin{pmatrix} 4 & -2 & 8 \\ -3 & 3 & 0 \end{pmatrix} - \begin{pmatrix} 1 & 7 & 6 \\ -2 & -8 & 5 \end{pmatrix} = \begin{pmatrix} 3 & -9 & 2 \\ -1 & 11 & -5 \end{pmatrix}$

# C Multiplication by a number
Multiply all the numbers in the matrix by the number outside, e.g. (1) $\begin{pmatrix} 4 & 3 \\ 0 & 6 \end{pmatrix} \times 3 = \begin{pmatrix} 12 & 9 \\ 0 & 18 \end{pmatrix}$

e.g. (2) $5 \begin{pmatrix} 2 & -1 \\ 3 & 0 \end{pmatrix} = \begin{pmatrix} 10 & -5 \\ 15 & 0 \end{pmatrix}$

e.g. (3) $\frac{1}{2} \begin{pmatrix} 12 & -8 \\ 7 & 26 \end{pmatrix} = \begin{pmatrix} 6 & -4 \\ 3\frac{1}{2} & 13 \end{pmatrix}$

# D Matrix patterns
A matrix with one row and two columns is a 1 x 2 matrix, e.g. (3 4); with two rows and three columns it is a 2 x 3 matrix, e.g.

$\begin{pmatrix} 1 & 5 & 1 \\ 2 & -4 & 0 \end{pmatrix}$ , etc.

**a** Try these additions

1) $(1 \quad 4) + (5 \quad 3)$

2) $\begin{pmatrix} 6 \\ 3 \end{pmatrix} + \begin{pmatrix} 2 \\ 7 \end{pmatrix}$

3) $(0 \quad 3) + (2 \quad 7)$

4) $\begin{pmatrix} 1 \\ 2 \\ 4 \end{pmatrix} + \begin{pmatrix} 6 \\ 3 \\ 11 \end{pmatrix}$

5) $\begin{pmatrix} -10 \\ 4 \end{pmatrix} + \begin{pmatrix} -2 \\ -4 \end{pmatrix}$

6) $\begin{pmatrix} 8 & 2 \\ 12 & 3 \end{pmatrix} + \begin{pmatrix} 5 & 11 \\ 1 & 10 \end{pmatrix}$

7) $\begin{pmatrix} 2 & 0 \\ 5 & -7 \end{pmatrix} + \begin{pmatrix} 4 & 1 \\ -3 & 3 \end{pmatrix}$

8) $(5 \quad 9 \quad -4) + (-5 \quad 9 \quad -4)$

9) $\begin{pmatrix} 4 & -7 \\ -3 & 4 \end{pmatrix} + \begin{pmatrix} 0 & 3 \\ 5 & -8 \end{pmatrix} + \begin{pmatrix} 1 & 2 \\ 2 & 1 \end{pmatrix}$

10) $\begin{pmatrix} 0 & 5 \\ 3 & -6 \\ 10 & 2 \end{pmatrix} + \begin{pmatrix} 7 & -4 \\ 1 & -2 \\ -1 & 6 \end{pmatrix}$

---

**b** Try these subtractions. Remember that − − has the same effect as +

1) $\begin{pmatrix} 5 \\ 7 \end{pmatrix} - \begin{pmatrix} 2 \\ 1 \end{pmatrix}$

2) $(6 \quad 9) - (6 \quad 5)$

3) $\begin{pmatrix} 1 & 4 \\ 3 & 7 \end{pmatrix} - \begin{pmatrix} 0 & 2 \\ 1 & 4 \end{pmatrix}$

4) $(6 \quad 2 \quad 3) - (2 \quad 5 \quad 0)$

5) $\begin{pmatrix} 5 \\ 6 \\ 1 \end{pmatrix} - \begin{pmatrix} 8 \\ 4 \\ 1 \end{pmatrix}$

6) $(4 \quad 3) - (-2 \quad 5)$

7) $\begin{pmatrix} 5 & 2 & -2 \\ 0 & 4 & 7 \end{pmatrix} - \begin{pmatrix} 1 & -2 & 2 \\ 4 & -1 & 6 \end{pmatrix}$

8) $\begin{pmatrix} -1 & -2 \\ -3 & -6 \end{pmatrix} - \begin{pmatrix} 2 & 4 \\ -4 & -6 \end{pmatrix}$

9) $(3 \quad 1 \quad -5) - (4 \quad -1 \quad 3)$

10) $\begin{pmatrix} 0 & 7 \\ 3 & 11 \\ 2 & 4 \end{pmatrix} - \begin{pmatrix} 7 & -1 \\ 0 & -8 \\ 1 & -3 \end{pmatrix}$

---

**c**

1) $\begin{pmatrix} 3 & 2 \\ 5 & 1 \end{pmatrix} \times 4$

2) $(5 \quad 7 \quad 2) \times 2$

3) $3\begin{pmatrix} 1 & 3 \\ 0 & -1 \end{pmatrix}$

4) $\begin{pmatrix} 1 & -1 \\ 2 & 2 \\ 3 & 0 \end{pmatrix} \times 5$

5) $6\begin{pmatrix} 3 & 2 & -1 \\ -1 & 1 & 0 \end{pmatrix}$

6) $\frac{1}{3}\begin{pmatrix} 6 & 3 & 15 \\ -12 & 0 & 9 \end{pmatrix}$

7) $4\begin{pmatrix} \frac{1}{2} & \frac{1}{4} \\ -1 & 1\frac{1}{2} \end{pmatrix}$

8) $-2\begin{pmatrix} 6 & 5 \\ 4 & -2 \\ -3 & 1 \end{pmatrix}$

9) $x\begin{pmatrix} 2 & x \\ y & 0 \end{pmatrix}$

10) $-\frac{1}{2}\begin{pmatrix} 8 & -2 & 14 \\ 4 & 0 & 16 \end{pmatrix}$

# A MATRICES (2) - MULTIPLICATION

## Compatible and incompatible matrices

Matrices may be multiplied only if they are COMPATIBLE for multiplication. The second matrix is PRE-MULTIPLIED by the first. **Each ROW in the first matrix must have the same pattern as each COLUMN in the second matrix,** e.g.

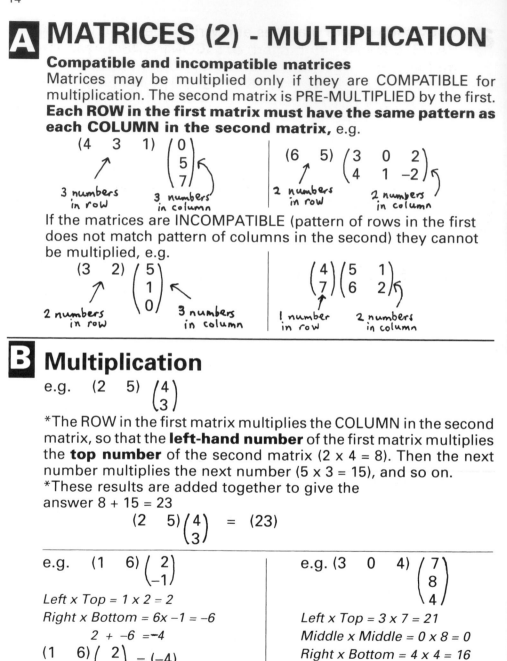

If the matrices are INCOMPATIBLE (pattern of rows in the first does not match pattern of columns in the second) they cannot be multiplied, e.g.

# B Multiplication

e.g.   $(2 \quad 5) \begin{pmatrix} 4 \\ 3 \end{pmatrix}$

*The ROW in the first matrix multiplies the COLUMN in the second matrix, so that the **left-hand number** of the first matrix multiplies the **top number** of the second matrix ($2 \times 4 = 8$). Then the next number multiplies the next number ($5 \times 3 = 15$), and so on.
*These results are added together to give the answer $8 + 15 = 23$

$$(2 \quad 5) \begin{pmatrix} 4 \\ 3 \end{pmatrix} = (23)$$

e.g.   $(1 \quad 6) \begin{pmatrix} 2 \\ -1 \end{pmatrix}$

*Left x Top = 1 x 2 = 2*
*Right x Bottom = 6x –1 = –6*

$2 + -6 = -4$

$$(1 \quad 6) \begin{pmatrix} 2 \\ -1 \end{pmatrix} = (-4)$$

e.g. $(3 \quad 0 \quad 4) \begin{pmatrix} 7 \\ 8 \\ 4 \end{pmatrix}$

*Left x Top = 3 x 7 = 21*
*Middle x Middle = 0 x 8 = 0*
*Right x Bottom = 4 x 4 = 16*
$21 + 0 + 16 = 37$

$$(3 \quad 0 \quad 4) \begin{pmatrix} 7 \\ 8 \\ 4 \end{pmatrix} = (37)$$

**a** Copy each pair of matrices and write whether it is COMPATIBLE (can be multiplied) or INCOMPATIBLE (cannot be multiplied)

1) $(5 \quad 3 \quad 7) \begin{pmatrix} 1 \\ 2 \\ 0 \end{pmatrix}$ 
2) $(2 \quad 4) \begin{pmatrix} 6 & 1 & 5 & 0 \\ 3 & 4 & 3 & 2 \end{pmatrix}$ 
3) $(6 \quad 0 \quad 1) \begin{pmatrix} 1 & 2 & 5 \\ 3 & 2 & -2 \end{pmatrix}$

4) $(6 \quad -1 \quad -2) \begin{pmatrix} 5 & 1 \\ 2 & 4 \\ 3 & 0 \end{pmatrix}$ 
5) $(8 \quad 7) \begin{pmatrix} 4 & 0 \\ 4 & 1 \\ -2 & 3 \end{pmatrix}$

**b** Multiply these matrices

1) $(4 \quad 3) \begin{pmatrix} 1 \\ 2 \end{pmatrix}$
2) $(5 \quad 0) \begin{pmatrix} 3 \\ 2 \end{pmatrix}$
3) $(6 \quad -1) \begin{pmatrix} 2 \\ 5 \end{pmatrix}$
4) $(5 \quad 2 \quad 3) \begin{pmatrix} 1 \\ 4 \\ 7 \end{pmatrix}$

5) $(0 \quad 3) \begin{pmatrix} 5 \\ 0 \end{pmatrix}$
6) $(4 \quad 1 \quad 2 \quad 2) \begin{pmatrix} 0 \\ 3 \\ 2 \\ -1 \end{pmatrix}$
7) $(-2 \quad -1) \begin{pmatrix} 4 \\ -6 \end{pmatrix}$
8) $(1 \quad 0 \quad 1) \begin{pmatrix} 12 \\ 3 \\ -6 \end{pmatrix}$

9) $(11 \quad 7 \quad 12) \begin{pmatrix} 6 \\ 0 \\ 1 \end{pmatrix}$
10) $(1 \quad 2 \quad 3) \begin{pmatrix} 3 \\ 2 \\ 1 \end{pmatrix}$

**c** Try these multiplications

1) $(4 \quad 8 \quad 2) \begin{pmatrix} 2 \\ 1 \\ 3 \end{pmatrix}$
2) $(5 \quad 5) \begin{pmatrix} 4 \\ 3 \end{pmatrix}$
3) $(-1 \quad 0 \quad 1 \quad 0) \begin{pmatrix} 3 \\ -3 \\ -2 \\ 1 \end{pmatrix}$
4) $(-4 \quad -6) \begin{pmatrix} -3 \\ -4 \end{pmatrix}$

5) $(3 \quad 19) \begin{pmatrix} 17 \\ 12 \end{pmatrix}$
6) $(0 \quad 5 \quad 2) \begin{pmatrix} 4 \\ 5 \\ 10 \end{pmatrix}$
7) $(-2 \quad -3 \quad 2) \begin{pmatrix} 7 \\ -6 \\ -2 \end{pmatrix}$

8) $(24 \quad -10) \begin{pmatrix} 10 \\ -16 \end{pmatrix}$
9) $(x \quad 3) \begin{pmatrix} 4 \\ x \end{pmatrix}$
10) $(6 \quad n \quad 2) \begin{pmatrix} n \\ 5 \\ 4 \end{pmatrix}$

# A MATRICES (3) - MULTIPLICATION

## Multiplication with several rows and columns
## What will the answer look like?

e.g. A **1** x 2 matrix 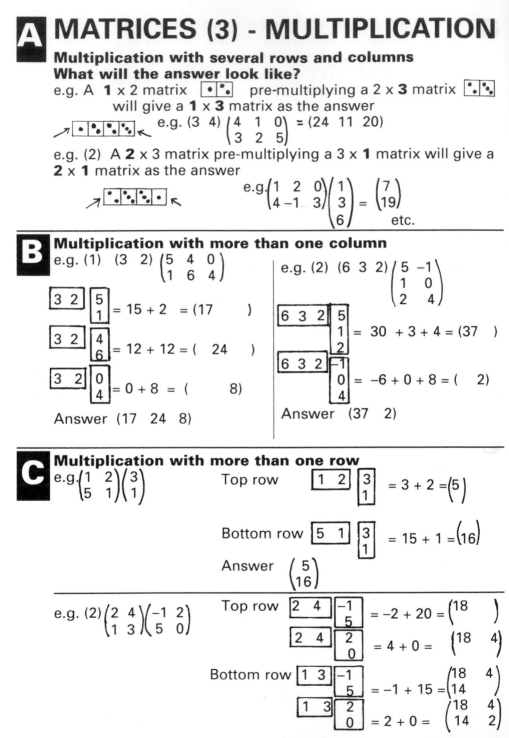 pre-multiplying a 2 x **3** matrix
will give a **1** x **3** matrix as the answer

e.g. $(3 \quad 4)\begin{pmatrix} 4 & 1 & 0 \\ 3 & 2 & 5 \end{pmatrix} = (24 \quad 11 \quad 20)$

e.g. (2) A **2** x 3 matrix pre-multiplying a 3 x **1** matrix will give a
**2** x **1** matrix as the answer

e.g. $\begin{pmatrix} 1 & 2 & 0 \\ 4 & -1 & 3 \end{pmatrix}\begin{pmatrix} 1 \\ 3 \\ 6 \end{pmatrix} = \begin{pmatrix} 7 \\ 19 \end{pmatrix}$ etc.

---

## B Multiplication with more than one column

e.g. (1) $(3 \quad 2)\begin{pmatrix} 5 & 4 & 0 \\ 1 & 6 & 4 \end{pmatrix}$

$\boxed{3 \ 2}\begin{bmatrix} 5 \\ 1 \end{bmatrix} = 15 + 2 = (17 \quad )$

$\boxed{3 \ 2}\begin{bmatrix} 4 \\ 6 \end{bmatrix} = 12 + 12 = ( \quad 24 \quad )$

$\boxed{3 \ 2}\begin{bmatrix} 0 \\ 4 \end{bmatrix} = 0 + 8 = ( \qquad 8)$

Answer $(17 \quad 24 \quad 8)$

e.g. (2) $(6 \ 3 \ 2)\begin{pmatrix} 5 & -1 \\ 1 & 0 \\ 2 & 4 \end{pmatrix}$

$\boxed{6 \ 3 \ 2}\begin{bmatrix} 5 \\ 1 \\ 2 \end{bmatrix} = 30 + 3 + 4 = (37 \quad )$

$\boxed{6 \ 3 \ 2}\begin{bmatrix} -1 \\ 0 \\ 4 \end{bmatrix} = -6 + 0 + 8 = ( \quad 2)$

Answer $(37 \quad 2)$

---

## C Multiplication with more than one row

e.g. $\begin{pmatrix} 1 & 2 \\ 5 & 1 \end{pmatrix}\begin{pmatrix} 3 \\ 1 \end{pmatrix}$

Top row $\boxed{1 \ 2}\begin{bmatrix} 3 \\ 1 \end{bmatrix} = 3 + 2 = \begin{pmatrix} 5 \end{pmatrix}$

Bottom row $\boxed{5 \ 1}\begin{bmatrix} 3 \\ 1 \end{bmatrix} = 15 + 1 = \begin{pmatrix} 16 \end{pmatrix}$

Answer $\begin{pmatrix} 5 \\ 16 \end{pmatrix}$

e.g. (2) $\begin{pmatrix} 2 & 4 \\ 1 & 3 \end{pmatrix}\begin{pmatrix} -1 & 2 \\ 5 & 0 \end{pmatrix}$

Top row $\boxed{2 \ 4}\begin{bmatrix} -1 \\ 5 \end{bmatrix} = -2 + 20 = \begin{pmatrix} 18 & \end{pmatrix}$

$\boxed{2 \ 4}\begin{bmatrix} 2 \\ 0 \end{bmatrix} = 4 + 0 = \begin{pmatrix} 18 & 4 \end{pmatrix}$

Bottom row $\boxed{1 \ 3}\begin{bmatrix} -1 \\ 5 \end{bmatrix} = -1 + 15 = \begin{pmatrix} 18 & 4 \\ 14 & \end{pmatrix}$

$\boxed{1 \ 3}\begin{bmatrix} 2 \\ 0 \end{bmatrix} = 2 + 0 = \begin{pmatrix} 18 & 4 \\ 14 & 2 \end{pmatrix}$

**a** Write down the pattern of matrix (e.g. 3 x 2) which will result from these multiplications

1) 1 x 3 premultiplying 3 x 1
2) 2 x 1 premultiplying 1 x 3
3) 3 x 2 premultiplying 2 x 2
4) 1 x 2 premultiplying 2 x 3
5) 2 x 3 premultiplying 3 x 2

6) 1 x 2 premultiplying 2 x 2
7) 4 x 1 premultiplying 1 x 3
8) 3 x 3 premultiplying 3 x 2
9) 2 x 4 premultiplying 4 x 5
10) 3 x 1 premultiplying 1 x 4

**b** Multiply these matrices

1) $(1 \quad 2) \begin{pmatrix} 3 & 4 \\ 1 & 0 \end{pmatrix}$

2) $(3 \quad 5) \begin{pmatrix} 2 & 1 \\ 1 & 6 \end{pmatrix}$

3) $(2 \quad 4) \begin{pmatrix} 1 & 2 & 0 \\ 0 & 3 & 5 \end{pmatrix}$

4) $(2 \quad 3 \quad 1) \begin{pmatrix} 4 & 3 \\ 1 & 0 \\ 2 & 1 \end{pmatrix}$

5) $(-1 \; -2) \begin{pmatrix} 3 & 1 \\ 7 & 2 \end{pmatrix}$

6) $(0 \; -1) \begin{pmatrix} 6 & 5 \\ 3 & 2 \end{pmatrix}$

7) $(6 \; -3) \begin{pmatrix} 0 & 3 & -2 \\ 1 & 2 & 2 \end{pmatrix}$

8) $(2 \quad 0 \quad 5) \begin{pmatrix} -2 & 2 & -3 \\ 9 & 4 & -1 \\ 3 & 1 & 2 \end{pmatrix}$

9) $(8 \; -1) \begin{pmatrix} 1 & 0 \\ 2 & -3 \end{pmatrix}$

10) $(-3 \; 1 \; -2) \begin{pmatrix} -2 \\ 4 \\ -5 \end{pmatrix}$

11) $(2 \; 1 \; 3 \; 4) \begin{pmatrix} 1 & 1 \\ 2 & -4 \\ 0 & 3 \\ 2 & 2 \end{pmatrix}$

12) $(15 \quad 22) \begin{pmatrix} 1 \\ -7 \end{pmatrix}$

13) $(2 \; -1 \; 3 \; 4) \begin{pmatrix} 4 \\ 1 \\ 2 \\ -3 \end{pmatrix}$

14) $(-1 \quad 1) \begin{pmatrix} 4 & 1 & 5 & 0 \\ 0 & 3 & 2 & 1 \end{pmatrix}$

15) $(3 \quad 2 \; -1) \begin{pmatrix} 1 & 3 & 0 \\ 2 & -1 & 5 \\ 4 & 3 & 1 \end{pmatrix}$

**c** Multiply these matrices

1) $\begin{pmatrix} 2 & 1 \\ 1 & 3 \end{pmatrix} \begin{pmatrix} 5 & 1 \\ 2 & 6 \end{pmatrix}$

2) $\begin{pmatrix} 4 & 0 \\ 0 & 3 \end{pmatrix} \begin{pmatrix} 1 & 2 \\ 4 & 3 \end{pmatrix}$

3) $\begin{pmatrix} 2 \\ 3 \end{pmatrix} (6 \quad 4)$

4) $\begin{pmatrix} 1 & 0 \\ 0 & 1 \end{pmatrix} \begin{pmatrix} 3 & 4 \\ 6 & 2 \end{pmatrix}$

5) $\begin{pmatrix} 2 & 6 \\ 3 & 7 \end{pmatrix} \begin{pmatrix} 5 \\ 4 \end{pmatrix}$

6) $\begin{pmatrix} 1 & 3 \\ 3 & 1 \end{pmatrix} \begin{pmatrix} 4 & 3 & 0 \\ 1 & 6 & 5 \end{pmatrix}$

7) $\begin{pmatrix} 8 \\ 2 \end{pmatrix} (3 \quad 5)$

8) $\begin{pmatrix} -1 & 0 \\ 2 & -1 \end{pmatrix} \begin{pmatrix} 3 & 4 \\ 6 & 2 \end{pmatrix}$

9) $\begin{pmatrix} 4 & 1 \\ 0 & 2 \\ 1 & 5 \end{pmatrix} \begin{pmatrix} 2 & 1 \\ 1 & 2 \end{pmatrix}$

10) $\begin{pmatrix} 2 & 4 & 1 \\ 1 & 2 & 3 \end{pmatrix} \begin{pmatrix} 6 \\ 1 \\ 2 \end{pmatrix}$

11) $\begin{pmatrix} 1 \\ 4 \\ 3 \end{pmatrix} (6 \quad 7)$

12) $\begin{pmatrix} -3 & 9 \\ 0 & -2 \end{pmatrix} \begin{pmatrix} -2 & 0 \\ 5 & -1 \end{pmatrix}$

13) $\begin{pmatrix} -1 & -2 \\ -4 & -1 \end{pmatrix} \begin{pmatrix} 0 & -1 & 1 \\ 1 & 0 & 0 \end{pmatrix}$

14) $\begin{pmatrix} 13 & 11 \\ 11 & 13 \end{pmatrix} \begin{pmatrix} 13 \\ 11 \end{pmatrix}$

15) $\begin{pmatrix} 3 & -1 \\ 0 & 2 \\ -1 & -2 \\ 2 & 4 \end{pmatrix} \begin{pmatrix} -2 & 3 & 0 \\ 1 & -4 & 1 \end{pmatrix}$

# A MATRICES (4)

## Determinant of a matrix

In the matrix $\begin{pmatrix} A & B \\ C & D \end{pmatrix}$ the determinant is $(A \times D) - (C \times B)$

e.g. the determinant of $\begin{pmatrix} 4 & 1 \\ 3 & 2 \end{pmatrix}$ is $(4 \times 2) - (3 \times 1) = 5$

e.g. the determinant of $\begin{pmatrix} 7 & -5 \\ -4 & 3 \end{pmatrix}$ is $(7 \times 3) - (-4 \times -5) = 1$

---

## B Inverse matrix of $\begin{pmatrix} A & B \\ C & D \end{pmatrix}$ is found by (i) changing the positions of A and D, (ii) making C and B negative, (iii) multiplying by the reciprocal of the determinant $\frac{1}{\text{determinant}}$

e.g. the inverse matrix of $\begin{pmatrix} 4 & 5 \\ 2 & 3 \end{pmatrix}$ which has determinant 2, is

$$\frac{1}{2}\begin{pmatrix} 3 & -5 \\ -2 & 4 \end{pmatrix} \quad \text{or} \quad \begin{pmatrix} 1\frac{1}{2} & -2\frac{1}{2} \\ -1 & 2 \end{pmatrix}$$

e.g. the inverse matrix of $\begin{pmatrix} 1 & -3 \\ -2 & 9 \end{pmatrix}$ which has determinant 3,

is $\quad \frac{1}{3}\begin{pmatrix} 9 & 3 \\ 2 & 1 \end{pmatrix} \quad \text{or} \quad \begin{pmatrix} 3 & 1 \\ \frac{2}{3} & \frac{1}{3} \end{pmatrix}$

---

## C Coded messages by matrices

Messages can be sent in code by using matrices. This form of coding is almost impossible to decode except by the person using the decoding matrix, e.g.

using $A = 1$, $B = 2$, $C = 3$, etc., the message PICKLE would be
16  9  3  11  12  5  which could be arranged into a
2 x 3 matrix $\begin{pmatrix} 16 & 9 & 3 \\ 11 & 12 & 5 \end{pmatrix}$

The sender of the message uses a coding matrix **with determinant 1**, e.g. $\begin{pmatrix} 2 & 1 \\ 5 & 3 \end{pmatrix}$ and the receiver uses

its INVERSE MATRIX $\begin{pmatrix} 3 & -1 \\ -5 & 2 \end{pmatrix}$

The sender premultiplies by the coding matrix

$$\begin{pmatrix} 2 & 1 \\ 5 & 3 \end{pmatrix} \begin{pmatrix} 16 & 9 & 3 \\ 11 & 12 & 5 \end{pmatrix} = \begin{pmatrix} 43 & 30 & 11 \\ 113 & 81 & 30 \end{pmatrix}$$

CODING MATRIX    MESSAGE    MESSAGE IN CODE

The receiver then premultiplies by the inverse (decoding) matrix

$$\begin{pmatrix} 3 & -1 \\ -5 & 2 \end{pmatrix} \begin{pmatrix} 43 & 30 & 11 \\ 113 & 81 & 30 \end{pmatrix} = \begin{pmatrix} 16 & 9 & 3 \\ 11 & 12 & 5 \end{pmatrix}$$

DECODING    MESSAGE IN CODE    MESSAGE
MATRIX

**a** Find the determinant of each of these matrices

1) $\begin{pmatrix} 4 & 1 \\ 7 & 2 \end{pmatrix}$

2) $\begin{pmatrix} 9 & 5 \\ 3 & 2 \end{pmatrix}$

3) $\begin{pmatrix} 3 & 1 \\ 1 & 3 \end{pmatrix}$

4) $\begin{pmatrix} 13 & 9 \\ 7 & 5 \end{pmatrix}$

5) $\begin{pmatrix} 2 & 1\frac{1}{2} \\ 1 & 1 \end{pmatrix}$

6) $\begin{pmatrix} 3 & 3 \\ 2 & 1 \end{pmatrix}$

7) $\begin{pmatrix} 3 & -4 \\ -2 & 3 \end{pmatrix}$

8) $\begin{pmatrix} 8 & 6 \\ 4 & 3 \end{pmatrix}$

9) $\begin{pmatrix} 6 & 3 \\ 3\frac{1}{2} & 2 \end{pmatrix}$

10) $\begin{pmatrix} 2 & 4 \\ -1 & 3 \end{pmatrix}$

---

**b** Find the inverse of each of these matrices. First find the determinant (d) of each matrix. Leave your answer in the form $\dfrac{1}{d}\begin{pmatrix} A & B \\ C & D \end{pmatrix}$

1) $\begin{pmatrix} 2 & 1 \\ 4 & 3 \end{pmatrix}$

2) $\begin{pmatrix} 5 & 6 \\ 6 & 4 \end{pmatrix}$

3) $\begin{pmatrix} 2 & 1 \\ -3 & 2 \end{pmatrix}$

4) $\begin{pmatrix} 9 & -3 \\ -5 & 2 \end{pmatrix}$

5) $\begin{pmatrix} 4 & 0 \\ 1 & 1 \end{pmatrix}$

6) $\begin{pmatrix} 2 & 3 \\ 1 & 2 \end{pmatrix}$

7) $\begin{pmatrix} 4 & -7 \\ -5 & 9 \end{pmatrix}$

8) $\begin{pmatrix} -2 & -3 \\ 3 & 7 \end{pmatrix}$

9) $\begin{pmatrix} 1 & 5 \\ \frac{1}{2} & 2 \end{pmatrix}$

10) $\begin{pmatrix} 4 & 5 \\ 5 & 7 \end{pmatrix}$

---

**c** Anthony sends messages to James using A = 1, B = 2, C = 3, D = 4, etc., and the coding matrix $\begin{pmatrix} 5 & 2 \\ 2 & 1 \end{pmatrix}$

The messages are (1) GO AWAY (2) HELP (3) STOP IT (4) DUCK (5) WELL DONE, and Anthony arranges them

1) $\begin{pmatrix} G & O & A \\ W & A & Y \end{pmatrix}$ 2) $\begin{pmatrix} H & E \\ L & P \end{pmatrix}$ 3) $\begin{pmatrix} S & T & O \\ P & I & T \end{pmatrix}$ 4) $\begin{pmatrix} D & U \\ C & K \end{pmatrix}$ 5) $\begin{pmatrix} W & E & L & L \\ D & O & N & E \end{pmatrix}$

(a) Write each message in number matrix form (b) Using Anthony's coding matrix, write each message in code

---

James uses the inverse matrix $\begin{pmatrix} 1 & -2 \\ -2 & 5 \end{pmatrix}$ to decode Anthony's messages. He receives these messages in code.

Try to work out what the messages are

6) $\begin{pmatrix} 125 & 37 & 112 \\ 53 & 16 & 46 \end{pmatrix}$

7) $\begin{pmatrix} 133 & 45 \\ 55 & 22 \end{pmatrix}$

8) $\begin{pmatrix} 38 & 75 & 124 & 63 \\ 16 & 33 & 51 & 29 \end{pmatrix}$

9) $\begin{pmatrix} 25 & 93 & 93 \\ 11 & 39 & 40 \end{pmatrix}$

10) $\begin{pmatrix} 99 & 85 & 7 & 136 & 33 \\ 40 & 37 & 3 & 58 & 14 \end{pmatrix}$

# A MATRICES (5)

## Solving equations using matrices

e.g. By multiplying matrices, find the value of y

$$(y \quad 5)\begin{pmatrix} 1 \\ y \end{pmatrix} = (18)$$

$$(1y + 5y) = (18)$$
$$(6y) = (18) \quad y = 3$$

e.g. (2) $\quad (k \quad 7)\begin{pmatrix} 3 \\ -2 \end{pmatrix} = (10)$

$$(3k - 14) = (10) \quad k = 8$$

## B Simultaneous equations in matrix form

e.g. Find the values of x and y if $\begin{pmatrix} 4 & x \\ y & 3 \end{pmatrix}\begin{pmatrix} 2 \\ 6 \end{pmatrix} = \begin{pmatrix} 32 \\ 22 \end{pmatrix}$

Top row x column gives $(4 \times 2) + (x \times 6) = 6x + 8$
Bottom row x column gives $(y \times 2) + (3 \times 6) = 2y + 18$

$$6x + 8 = 32$$
$$2y + 18 \quad 22$$

From the top row $6x + 8 = 32$, so $x = 4$ $\quad \begin{cases} x = 4 \\ y = 2 \end{cases}$
From the bottom row $2y + 18 = 22$, so $y = 2$

Try checking the answer by substituting for x and y in the original matrix $\begin{pmatrix} 4 & 4 \\ 2 & 3 \end{pmatrix}\begin{pmatrix} 2 \\ 6 \end{pmatrix} = \begin{pmatrix} 32 \\ 22 \end{pmatrix}$

## C Solving simultaneous equations by matrices

e.g. $\quad 2x + 7y = 13$
$\quad\quad\quad x + 5y = 8$

*Write in matrix form $\begin{pmatrix} 2 & 7 \\ 1 & 5 \end{pmatrix}\begin{pmatrix} x \\ y \end{pmatrix} = \begin{pmatrix} 13 \\ 8 \end{pmatrix}$

*Multiply both sides of the equation by the inverse matrix

$$\frac{1}{3}\begin{pmatrix} 5 & -7 \\ -1 & 2 \end{pmatrix}\begin{pmatrix} 2 & 7 \\ 1 & 5 \end{pmatrix}\begin{pmatrix} x \\ y \end{pmatrix} = \frac{1}{3}\begin{pmatrix} 5 & -7 \\ -1 & 2 \end{pmatrix}\begin{pmatrix} 13 \\ 8 \end{pmatrix}$$

$$\begin{pmatrix} x \\ y \end{pmatrix} = \frac{1}{3}\begin{pmatrix} 9 \\ 3 \end{pmatrix}$$

$$\begin{pmatrix} x \\ y \end{pmatrix} = \begin{pmatrix} 3 \\ 1 \end{pmatrix} \quad \begin{cases} x = 3 \\ y = 1 \end{cases}$$

NOTE. Any matrix multiplied by its inverse matrix gives the matrix form of the number 1, e.g. in the above example

$$\frac{1}{3}\begin{pmatrix} 5 & -7 \\ -1 & 2 \end{pmatrix}\begin{pmatrix} 2 & 7 \\ 1 & 5 \end{pmatrix}\begin{pmatrix} x \\ y \end{pmatrix} = \begin{pmatrix} 1 & 0 \\ 0 & 1 \end{pmatrix}\begin{pmatrix} x \\ y \end{pmatrix} = \begin{pmatrix} x \\ y \end{pmatrix} \quad , \text{etc.}$$

## a  Solve these equations

1) $(a \quad 3) \begin{pmatrix} 4 \\ a \end{pmatrix} = (21)$

2) $(5 \quad c) \begin{pmatrix} c \\ 4 \end{pmatrix} = (9)$

3) $(2 \quad t \quad 3) \begin{pmatrix} t \\ 6 \\ 1 \end{pmatrix} = (19)$

4) $\begin{pmatrix} d & 4 \\ 1 & d \end{pmatrix} \begin{pmatrix} 2 \\ 0 \end{pmatrix} = \begin{pmatrix} 12 \\ 2 \end{pmatrix}$

5) $(h \quad 2) \begin{pmatrix} 6 \\ -3 \end{pmatrix} = (0)$

6) $(7 \quad 2) \begin{pmatrix} 5 \\ a \end{pmatrix} = (19)$

7) $(m \quad 1) \begin{pmatrix} 1 \\ 1 \end{pmatrix} = (0)$

8) $(2x \quad 3) \begin{pmatrix} 1 \\ -4 \end{pmatrix} = (10)$

9) $(-2 \quad -5) \begin{pmatrix} -4 \\ f \end{pmatrix} = (28)$

10) $(y \quad 3) \begin{pmatrix} y \\ 2 \end{pmatrix} = (22)$

## b  Find the values of x and y in each of these

1) $\begin{pmatrix} x & 2 \\ 3 & y \end{pmatrix} \begin{pmatrix} 4 \\ 5 \end{pmatrix} = \begin{pmatrix} 18 \\ 17 \end{pmatrix}$

2) $\begin{pmatrix} x & 0 \\ 0 & y \end{pmatrix} \begin{pmatrix} 3 \\ 2 \end{pmatrix} = \begin{pmatrix} 9 \\ 10 \end{pmatrix}$

3) $\begin{pmatrix} x & -1 \\ 3 & y \end{pmatrix} \begin{pmatrix} 2 \\ 4 \end{pmatrix} = \begin{pmatrix} 8 \\ 10 \end{pmatrix}$

4) $\begin{pmatrix} x & 2 \\ 1 & y \end{pmatrix} \begin{pmatrix} 4 \\ 3 \end{pmatrix} = \begin{pmatrix} 26 \\ 25 \end{pmatrix}$

5) $\begin{pmatrix} -3 & x \\ y & -2 \end{pmatrix} \begin{pmatrix} 1 \\ 5 \end{pmatrix} = \begin{pmatrix} 17 \\ 1 \end{pmatrix}$

6) $(x \quad 1) \begin{pmatrix} 5 & 2 \\ 1 & y \end{pmatrix} = (41 \quad 21)$

7) $\begin{pmatrix} 6 & x \\ y & 7 \end{pmatrix} \begin{pmatrix} 4 \\ -2 \end{pmatrix} = \begin{pmatrix} 10 \\ 10 \end{pmatrix}$

8) $\begin{pmatrix} 5 & 0 \\ 0 & 4 \end{pmatrix} \begin{pmatrix} x \\ y \end{pmatrix} = \begin{pmatrix} 20 \\ 12 \end{pmatrix}$

9) $\begin{pmatrix} 1 & y \\ x & 2 \end{pmatrix} \begin{pmatrix} 6 \\ 5 \end{pmatrix} = \begin{pmatrix} -4 \\ 4 \end{pmatrix}$

10) $\begin{pmatrix} x & y \\ y & x \end{pmatrix} \begin{pmatrix} 3 \\ 2 \end{pmatrix} = \begin{pmatrix} 14 \\ 16 \end{pmatrix}$

## c  Write these simultaneous equations in matrix form and solve them

1) $3x + y = 9$
$x + 2y = 8$

2) $4x + y = 8$
$7x + 2y = 15$

3) $3x + 7y = 23$
$x + 3y = 9$

4) $5x - y = 3$
$-2x + y = 0$

5) $3x + y = 10$
$8x + 3y = 27$

6) $5x + 6y = 38$
$2x + 3y = 17$

7) $3x - y = 7$
$2x + y = 3$

8) $2x + 3y = 25$
$x + 2y = 15$

9) $x + 3y = 7$
$3x + 13y = 25$

10) $3x - y = 12$
$5x + 2y = 9$

# A MATRICES (6)

## Information store

Matrices are sometimes used as a short, compact way of storing, or showing, information,

e.g. Garside School has four soccer teams: 1st, 2nd, 3rd and Junior. Their results last season (win, lose or draw) can be shown as a matrix

$$\begin{array}{c} \\ W \\ L \\ D \end{array} \begin{array}{cccc} 1st & 2nd & 3rd & Jun \\ \left(\begin{array}{cccc} 9 & 3 & 4 & 6 \\ 5 & 4 & 4 & 0 \\ 2 & 3 & 1 & 3 \end{array}\right) \end{array}$$

This matrix shows that the 1st team won 9 times, lost 5 times and drew twice, etc.

In the local schools league, a win counts 3 points, a loss counts 1 point and a draw counts 2 points. If the results matrix is premultiplied by (3  1  2), a new matrix is obtained.

$$\begin{array}{c} \\ Points \end{array} \begin{array}{c} W \ L \ D \\ \left(\begin{array}{ccc} 3 & 1 & 2 \end{array}\right) \end{array} \begin{array}{c} \\ W \\ L \\ D \end{array} \begin{array}{c} 1st\,2nd\ 3rd\,Jun \\ \left(\begin{array}{cccc} 9 & 3 & 4 & 6 \\ 5 & 4 & 4 & 0 \\ 2 & 3 & 1 & 3 \end{array}\right) \end{array} = Points \begin{array}{c} 1st\ 2nd\ 3rd\ Jun \\ \left(\begin{array}{cccc} 36 & 19 & 18 & 24 \end{array}\right) \end{array}$$

The new matrix shows the total points gained by each team, e.g. 1st team 36 points, etc.

If, instead, the results matrix were premultiplied by (1  1  1) what information would the new matrix give?

---

e.g. (2) The Walker family buy bottles of milk, tubs of cream and cartons of yogurt from the milkman. The items they bought last week can be shown as a 3 x 6 matrix

(M=Monday, etc.)

$$\begin{array}{c} \\ Milk \\ Cream \\ Yogurt \end{array} \begin{array}{cccccc} M & Tu & W & Th & F & S \\ \left(\begin{array}{cccccc} 4 & 3 & 3 & 2 & 4 & 6 \\ 2 & 0 & 2 & 0 & 1 & 2 \\ 8 & 4 & 6 & 4 & 0 & 10 \end{array}\right) \end{array}$$

This matrix shows that on Monday the Walkers bought 4 bottles of milk, 2 tubs of cream and 8 cartons of yogurt, etc.

Milk costs 30p a bottle, cream costs 42p a tub and yogurt costs 25p a carton. Premultiplying by (30 42 25) gives the total cost, in pence, for each day's supply

$$(30 \ 42 \ 25)\left(\begin{array}{cccccc} 4 & 3 & 3 & 2 & 4 & 6 \\ 2 & 0 & 2 & 0 & 1 & 2 \\ 8 & 4 & 6 & 4 & 0 & 10 \end{array}\right) = (404 \ 190 \ 324 \ 160 \ 162 \ 514)$$

What information would be given by multiplying the following matrices?

$$(404 \ 190 \ 324 \ 160 \ 162 \ 514)\left(\begin{array}{c} 1 \\ 1 \\ 1 \\ 1 \\ 1 \\ 1 \end{array}\right)$$

**a**

1) (a) At an athletics meeting, Spilman Street School gained 5 first places, 6 seconds and 3 thirds. Lowe Road School gained 4 firsts, 8 seconds and 2 thirds. Write this information as a 3 x 2 matrix P.

(b) There are 5 points for a first, 3 for a second and 1 for a third. Write this as a 1 x 3 matrix Q.

(c) Multiply QP to see which school won.

---

2) A hotel offers three classes of accommodation: A, B and C. During a certain month the number of guests and class of accommodation chosen were: Week 1, 9 class A, 6 class B, 3 class C; week 2. 10A, 2B, 5C; week 3, 6A, 4B, 6C; week 4, 6A, 5B, 7C.

(i) Write this information as a 3 x 4 matrix N.

(ii) Class A costs £14 a week, B costs £22 and C costs £27. Write this information as a 1 x 3 matrix M.

(iii) Multiply MN and explain what information the answer gives.

---

3) (a) During a series of rugby matches the 1st XV scored 12 tries, 5 goals and 6 conversions. The 2nd XV scored 10 tries, 3 goals and 4 conversions. Write these results as a 2 x 3 matrix A.

(b) A try gains 4 points, a goal 3 points and a conversion 2 points. Write this as a 3 x 1 matrix B.

(c) Multiply AB and explain what the answer means.

---

4) (a) A tollbridge charges for each vehicle which uses it. The charge is £2 for a car, £1 for a motorcycle and £4 for a lorry or bus. Write these charges as a 1 x 3 matrix C.

(b) On a certain day 433 cars, 28 motorcycles and 174 lorries and buses pass over the bridge. Write these figures as a 3 x 1 matrix D.

(c) Multiply CD and say what the answer means.

(d) E is the matrix ( 1  1  1 ). Multiply ED and say what the answer means.

---

5) (a) At the sweet shop, Ben bought 3 toffee bars, 5 lollies and 12 fruit sweets; Lucy bought 4 toffee bars, 3 lollies and 7 fruit sweets. Write this information as a 2 x 3 matrix K.

(b) Toffee bars are 11p each, lollies 6p each and fruit sweets 3p each. Write this as a 3 x 1 matrix L.

(c) Multiply KL to give M. What information does M show?

(d) Premultiply M by the matrix ( $\frac{1}{2}$  $\frac{1}{2}$ ) to give N, and explain what information N gives.

# A MATRICES (7)

## Matrix transformations

Certain matrices can be used to show transformations (reflections or rotations),

e.g.

The point A in the drawing has coordinates (3, 2)

The coordinates of A may also be written as a matrix $\begin{pmatrix} 3 \\ 2 \end{pmatrix}$. By premultiplying by the matrix $\begin{pmatrix} 1 & 0 \\ 0 & -1 \end{pmatrix}$ a new matrix is formed $\begin{pmatrix} 1 & 0 \\ 0 & -1 \end{pmatrix}\begin{pmatrix} 3 \\ 2 \end{pmatrix} = \begin{pmatrix} 3 \\ -2 \end{pmatrix}$

The new matrix represents a new point with coordinates (3, −2)

The new point is the reflection of A in the x axis.

e.g. (2) The corners of a triangle PQR have coordinates P (1, 1), Q (2, 1), R (1, 3). Write these coordinates as a 2 x 3 matrix. Then premultiply the matrix by $\begin{pmatrix} -1 & 0 \\ 0 & -1 \end{pmatrix}$

From your answer, describe how the triangle PQR has been transformed. $\begin{pmatrix} -1 & 0 \\ 0 & -1 \end{pmatrix}\begin{pmatrix} 1 & 2 & 1 \\ 1 & 1 & 3 \end{pmatrix} = \begin{pmatrix} -1 & -2 & -1 \\ -1 & -1 & -3 \end{pmatrix}$

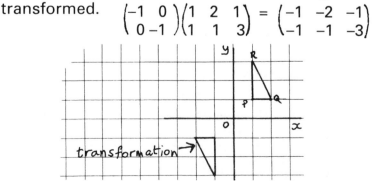

Triangle PQR has been rotated 180° about 0.

**a** Use squared paper to answer these questions (1cm squares are probably best). For each question, first draw x and y axes from –6 to +6 each.

1) Plot points A (5, 2), B (1, 4), C (1, 2). Join the points to form a triangle. Write these coordinates as a 2 x 3 matrix and premultiply by $\begin{pmatrix} -1 & 0 \\ 0 & 1 \end{pmatrix}$. Plot the new points to show the image of ABC.
Describe in words how ABC has been transformed.

2) Plot points J (3, 5), K (2, 5), L(2 ,2), M(5, 2) and join to form a quadrilateral. Write the coordinates as a 2 x 4 matrix and pre multiply by $\begin{pmatrix} 0 & 1 \\ -1 & 0 \end{pmatrix}$.
Plot the quadrilateral which is the image of JKLM and describe the transformation which JKLM has undergone.

3) Plot points D (4, 1), E (4, 4), F (6, 2). Join these points to form a triangle DEF. Write the coordinates as a matrix and pre multiply by $\begin{pmatrix} 0 & 1 \\ 1 & 0 \end{pmatrix}$.
Plot the coordinates given by your answer and join to form a triangle.
What is the graph of the line in which DEF is reflected?

4) Repeat question 3, using the same axes, but premultiply instead by $\begin{pmatrix} 0 & -1 \\ -1 & 0 \end{pmatrix}$. Describe this transformation.

5) Draw a triangle with corners (–1, 4), (–5, 2), (–3, 2) and write these coordinates as a matrix. Premultiply by $\begin{pmatrix} 0 & -1 \\ 1 & 0 \end{pmatrix}$ and plot the position of the new triangle given by your answer.

6) Plot points (–2, –1), (–4, –1), (–2, –2) to form a triangle A. Arrange the coordinates as a 2 x 3 matrix and premultiply by $\begin{pmatrix} 1 & 0 \\ 0 & -1 \end{pmatrix}$.
Draw the new triangle B.
What transformation does $\begin{pmatrix} 1 & 0 \\ 0 & -1 \end{pmatrix}$ represent?

7) Repeat question 6, using the same axes, but premultiply instead by $\begin{pmatrix} -1 & 0 \\ 0 & -1 \end{pmatrix}$. Describe this transformation.

8) Draw triangle P $= \begin{pmatrix} 2 & 4 & 2 \\ -5 & -4 & -4 \end{pmatrix}$. Premultiply by M $= \begin{pmatrix} 0 & -1 \\ 1 & 0 \end{pmatrix}$ to give Q. Draw the triangle represented by Q. Premultiply Q by N $\begin{pmatrix} 0 & 1 \\ 1 & 0 \end{pmatrix}$ to give R. Draw the triangle represented by R.
By multiplying NM find the single matrix which maps P on to R. Describe the transformations P to Q, Q to R, P to R.

9) Draw triangle P (2, 1), Q (3, 1), R (3, 3) and write as a 2 x 3 matrix. Premultiply by $\begin{pmatrix} 2 & 0 \\ 0 & 2 \end{pmatrix}$ and draw the result.
(a) How does the length of the new figure compare with the original?
(b) How does the area of the new figure compare with the original?
(c) What is this kind of transformation called?

10) Draw a figure with any coordinates. Write these in matrix form and premultiply by $\begin{pmatrix} 1 & 1 \\ 1 & 1 \end{pmatrix}$.
What is the graph of the line produced by your answer?

# A VECTORS (1)

A VECTOR is the movement of a point in a straight line from one position to another. A vector has **size** (usually called MAGNITUDE or LENGTH) and **direction**.

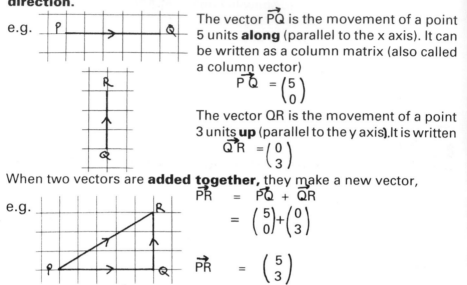

e.g.

The vector $\overrightarrow{PQ}$ is the movement of a point 5 units **along** (parallel to the x axis). It can be written as a column matrix (also called a column vector)

$$\overrightarrow{PQ} = \begin{pmatrix} 5 \\ 0 \end{pmatrix}$$

The vector QR is the movement of a point 3 units **up** (parallel to the y axis). It is written

$$\overrightarrow{QR} = \begin{pmatrix} 0 \\ 3 \end{pmatrix}$$

When two vectors are **added together,** they make a new vector,

e.g.

$$\overrightarrow{PR} = \overrightarrow{PQ} + \overrightarrow{QR}$$
$$= \begin{pmatrix} 5 \\ 0 \end{pmatrix} + \begin{pmatrix} 0 \\ 3 \end{pmatrix}$$
$$\overrightarrow{PR} = \begin{pmatrix} 5 \\ 3 \end{pmatrix}$$

In this drawing, $\overrightarrow{PQ}$ and $\overrightarrow{QR}$ are COMPONENT vectors and $\overrightarrow{PR}$ is the RESULTANT vector.

The vector $\overrightarrow{RP} = \begin{pmatrix} -5 \\ -3 \end{pmatrix}$. It has the same magnitude as $\overrightarrow{PR}$ but goes in the opposite direction.

Vectors are shown in writing
either (1) as two letters with an arrow on top, e.g. $\overrightarrow{AB}$
    or (2) as a small letter, e.g. **a**

Vectors are shown in drawings as straight lines with arrows on them

e.g.

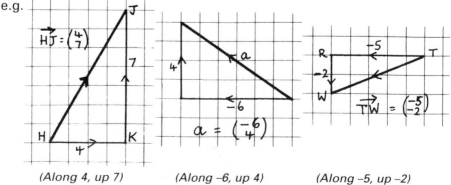

$\overrightarrow{HJ} = \begin{pmatrix} 4 \\ 7 \end{pmatrix}$

$a = \begin{pmatrix} -6 \\ 4 \end{pmatrix}$

$\overrightarrow{TW} = \begin{pmatrix} -5 \\ -2 \end{pmatrix}$

(Along 4, up 7)        (Along –6, up 4)        (Along –5, up –2)

**a** On squared paper (1 cm squares are probably best) draw these vectors. Remember to put an arrow to show the direction of each vector.

1) $\overrightarrow{AB} = \begin{pmatrix} 6 \\ 0 \end{pmatrix}$     5) $\overrightarrow{DG} = \begin{pmatrix} 0 \\ 3 \end{pmatrix}$     9) $\overrightarrow{WV} = \begin{pmatrix} 0 \\ 9 \end{pmatrix}$

2) $\overrightarrow{MN} = \begin{pmatrix} 2 \\ 0 \end{pmatrix}$     6) $\overrightarrow{KM} = \begin{pmatrix} 0 \\ 7 \end{pmatrix}$     10) $\overrightarrow{EF} = \begin{pmatrix} 0 \\ -6 \end{pmatrix}$

3) $\overrightarrow{XY} = \begin{pmatrix} 4 \\ 0 \end{pmatrix}$     7) $\overrightarrow{HN} = \begin{pmatrix} 0 \\ 4 \end{pmatrix}$

4) $\overrightarrow{TV} = \begin{pmatrix} -5 \\ 0 \end{pmatrix}$     8) $\overrightarrow{CA} = \begin{pmatrix} -1 \\ 0 \end{pmatrix}$

**b** Add each pair of vectors. Write the answers as a new vector and draw a diagram showing the component vectors and the resultant vector.

1) $\begin{pmatrix} 4 \\ 0 \end{pmatrix} + \begin{pmatrix} 0 \\ 3 \end{pmatrix}$     3) $\begin{pmatrix} 3 \\ 0 \end{pmatrix} + \begin{pmatrix} 0 \\ -5 \end{pmatrix}$     5) $\begin{pmatrix} -6 \\ 0 \end{pmatrix} + \begin{pmatrix} 0 \\ -4 \end{pmatrix}$

2) $\begin{pmatrix} 5 \\ 0 \end{pmatrix} + \begin{pmatrix} 0 \\ 6 \end{pmatrix}$     4) $\begin{pmatrix} -7 \\ 0 \end{pmatrix} + \begin{pmatrix} 0 \\ 4 \end{pmatrix}$

**c** Draw these vectors on squared paper

1) $a = \begin{pmatrix} 6 \\ 2 \end{pmatrix}$     5) $\overrightarrow{RP} = \begin{pmatrix} -4 \\ 3 \end{pmatrix}$     9) $\overrightarrow{XZ} = \begin{pmatrix} -1 \\ -7 \end{pmatrix}$

2) $\overrightarrow{LM} = \begin{pmatrix} 1 \\ 7 \end{pmatrix}$     6) $h = \begin{pmatrix} 2 \\ 8 \end{pmatrix}$     10) $q = \begin{pmatrix} 3 \\ -4 \end{pmatrix}$

3) $c = \begin{pmatrix} 5 \\ 5 \end{pmatrix}$     7) $\overrightarrow{JK} = \begin{pmatrix} -2 \\ -5 \end{pmatrix}$

4) $b = \begin{pmatrix} 4 \\ -2 \end{pmatrix}$     8) $m = \begin{pmatrix} -6 \\ 9 \end{pmatrix}$

**d** Write down the column vector represented by each of these

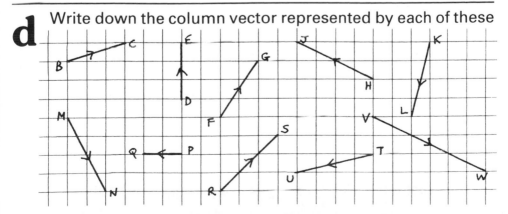

# A VECTORS (2)

### Addition of 'sloping' vectors

e.g. Add the vectors $\begin{pmatrix} 2 \\ 4 \end{pmatrix}$ and $\begin{pmatrix} 6 \\ 1 \end{pmatrix}$. Write the answer as a new column vector and draw a diagram to represent the sum.

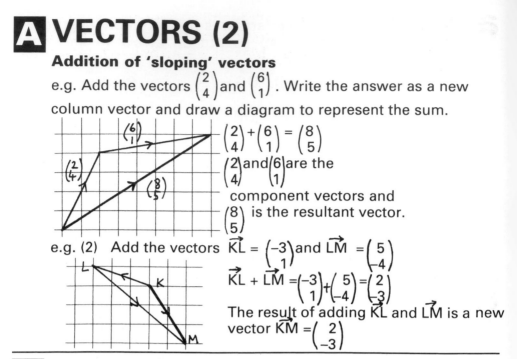

$\begin{pmatrix} 2 \\ 4 \end{pmatrix} + \begin{pmatrix} 6 \\ 1 \end{pmatrix} = \begin{pmatrix} 8 \\ 5 \end{pmatrix}$

$\begin{pmatrix} 2 \\ 4 \end{pmatrix}$ and $\begin{pmatrix} 6 \\ 1 \end{pmatrix}$ are the component vectors and $\begin{pmatrix} 8 \\ 5 \end{pmatrix}$ is the resultant vector.

e.g. (2)   Add the vectors $\overrightarrow{KL} = \begin{pmatrix} -3 \\ 1 \end{pmatrix}$ and $\overrightarrow{LM} = \begin{pmatrix} 5 \\ -4 \end{pmatrix}$

$\overrightarrow{KL} + \overrightarrow{LM} = \begin{pmatrix} -3 \\ 1 \end{pmatrix} + \begin{pmatrix} 5 \\ -4 \end{pmatrix} = \begin{pmatrix} 2 \\ -3 \end{pmatrix}$

The result of adding $\overrightarrow{KL}$ and $\overrightarrow{LM}$ is a new vector $\overrightarrow{KM} = \begin{pmatrix} 2 \\ -3 \end{pmatrix}$

## B Arrow direction in vector triangles

In a vector triangle, the arrow on the resultant vector goes round the triangle the opposite way to the arrows on the component vectors.

e.g. In the triangle PQR, which is the resultant vector?

The arrows on $\overrightarrow{PQ}$ and $\overrightarrow{QR}$ go clockwise. The arrow on $\overrightarrow{PR}$ goes anticlockwise (the opposite way), so **$\overrightarrow{PR}$ is the resultant vector.**

The resultant is the direct route (short cut) from start to finish. It is often marked with TWO arrows to make it clear.

## C Vector addition, subtraction and multiplication

e.g. If a is the vector $\begin{pmatrix} 3 \\ 4 \end{pmatrix}$, b is the vector $\begin{pmatrix} 2 \\ -1 \end{pmatrix}$

the vector 2a is $2 \begin{pmatrix} 3 \\ 4 \end{pmatrix} = \begin{pmatrix} 6 \\ 8 \end{pmatrix}$

the vector 3b is $3 \begin{pmatrix} 2 \\ -1 \end{pmatrix} = \begin{pmatrix} 6 \\ -3 \end{pmatrix}$

the vector a + 2b is $\begin{pmatrix} 3 \\ 4 \end{pmatrix} + \begin{pmatrix} 4 \\ -2 \end{pmatrix} = \begin{pmatrix} 7 \\ 2 \end{pmatrix}$

the vector b − a is $\begin{pmatrix} 2 \\ -1 \end{pmatrix} - \begin{pmatrix} 3 \\ 4 \end{pmatrix} = \begin{pmatrix} -1 \\ -5 \end{pmatrix}$     etc.

**a** Add each pair of vectors. Write the answer as a new column vector. Then draw a diagram, showing the component vectors and the resultant vector. Make sure arrows are facing the correct ways.

1) $\begin{pmatrix} 4 \\ 1 \end{pmatrix} + \begin{pmatrix} 2 \\ 2 \end{pmatrix}$    6) $\begin{pmatrix} 1 \\ 5 \end{pmatrix} + \begin{pmatrix} 4 \\ 0 \end{pmatrix}$    11) $\begin{pmatrix} 0 \\ -3 \end{pmatrix} + \begin{pmatrix} 3 \\ 5 \end{pmatrix}$

2) $\begin{pmatrix} 5 \\ 2 \end{pmatrix} + \begin{pmatrix} 1 \\ 3 \end{pmatrix}$    7) $\begin{pmatrix} -2 \\ 2 \end{pmatrix} + \begin{pmatrix} 6 \\ 1 \end{pmatrix}$    12) $\begin{pmatrix} -3 \\ 2 \end{pmatrix} + \begin{pmatrix} 3 \\ -7 \end{pmatrix}$

3) $\begin{pmatrix} 3 \\ 3 \end{pmatrix} + \begin{pmatrix} 0 \\ 2 \end{pmatrix}$    8) $\begin{pmatrix} 2 \\ -3 \end{pmatrix} + \begin{pmatrix} -4 \\ -2 \end{pmatrix}$    13) $\begin{pmatrix} 4 \\ -2 \end{pmatrix} + \begin{pmatrix} -5 \\ 8 \end{pmatrix}$

4) $\begin{pmatrix} 3 \\ 2 \end{pmatrix} + \begin{pmatrix} 4 \\ 1 \end{pmatrix}$    9) $\begin{pmatrix} -3 \\ 3 \end{pmatrix} + \begin{pmatrix} 2 \\ -5 \end{pmatrix}$    14) $\begin{pmatrix} -3 \\ -1 \end{pmatrix} + \begin{pmatrix} 5 \\ 5 \end{pmatrix}$

5) $\begin{pmatrix} 2 \\ 2 \end{pmatrix} + \begin{pmatrix} -4 \\ 2 \end{pmatrix}$    10) $\begin{pmatrix} 3 \\ 4 \end{pmatrix} + \begin{pmatrix} 1 \\ 4 \end{pmatrix}$    15) $\begin{pmatrix} 9 \\ 2 \end{pmatrix} + \begin{pmatrix} -4 \\ -4 \end{pmatrix}$

**b** Write down which is the resultant vector in each of these

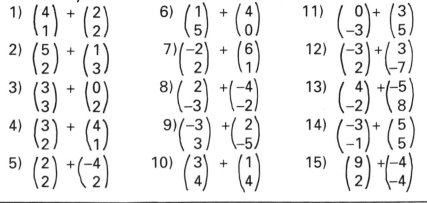

1)   2)   3)   4)

5)   6)   7)

8)   9)   10)

**c** If $a = \begin{pmatrix} 3 \\ 1 \end{pmatrix}$,   $b = \begin{pmatrix} 1 \\ -1 \end{pmatrix}$,   $c = \begin{pmatrix} -2 \\ 3 \end{pmatrix}$,   work out these
and write them as column vectors.

1)   2a       6)   a − c       11)   2b − 3c

2)   3b       7)   2b + a      12)   c − b

3)   5c       8)   2c + 4b     13)   a + b + c

4)   a + b     9)   3a + c      14)   4c − 2a

5)   b + c     10)   −4b       15)   5b + 2c

# A VECTORS (3)

## Drawing + − x of vectors

e.g. a is the vector $\begin{pmatrix} 1 \\ 2 \end{pmatrix}$, b is the vector $\begin{pmatrix} 3 \\ -1 \end{pmatrix}$

$\overrightarrow{HJ} = 2a$, $\overrightarrow{HK} = b$. (i) Draw the vectors $\overrightarrow{HJ}$, $\overrightarrow{HK}$ and $\overrightarrow{JK}$.

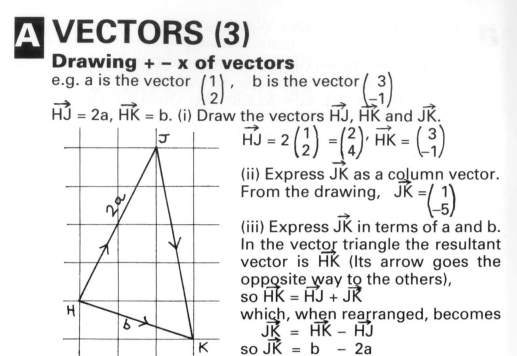

$\overrightarrow{HJ} = 2\begin{pmatrix} 1 \\ 2 \end{pmatrix} = \begin{pmatrix} 2 \\ 4 \end{pmatrix}$, $\overrightarrow{HK} = \begin{pmatrix} 3 \\ -1 \end{pmatrix}$

(ii) Express $\overrightarrow{JK}$ as a column vector.
From the drawing, $\overrightarrow{JK} = \begin{pmatrix} 1 \\ -5 \end{pmatrix}$

(iii) Express $\overrightarrow{JK}$ in terms of a and b.
In the vector triangle the resultant vector is $\overrightarrow{HK}$ (Its arrow goes the opposite way to the others),
so $\overrightarrow{HK} = \overrightarrow{HJ} + \overrightarrow{JK}$
which, when rearranged, becomes
$\overrightarrow{JK} = \overrightarrow{HK} - \overrightarrow{HJ}$
so $\overrightarrow{JK} = b - 2a$

---

# B Magnitude of a vector

The MAGNITUDE (or LENGTH) of a 'horizontal' or 'vertical' vector, i.e. one whose column vector contains a zero, can be drawn and measured simply, e.g.

Vector $\overrightarrow{RS} = \begin{pmatrix} 5 \\ 0 \end{pmatrix}$     Vector $\overrightarrow{DC} = \begin{pmatrix} 0 \\ -3 \end{pmatrix}$

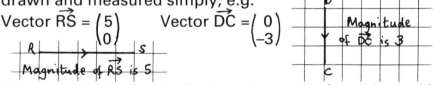

The magnitude of a 'sloping' vector can be found by making the vector the hypotenuse of a right-angled triangle and using Pythagoras' theorem (see page 4),
e.g. vector $\overrightarrow{GJ} = \begin{pmatrix} 4 \\ 2 \end{pmatrix}$

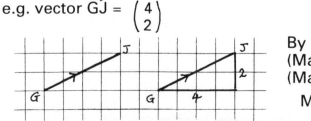

By Pythagoras
$(\text{Mag } \overrightarrow{GJ})^2 = 4^2 + 2^2$
$(\text{Mag } \overrightarrow{GJ})^2 = 16 + 4$
$\text{Mag } \overrightarrow{GJ} = \sqrt{20}$

When working out magnitude, the direction of the vector does not matter. The magnitude of a vector is NEVER negative.

**a**

1) $a = \begin{pmatrix} 3 \\ 1 \end{pmatrix}$, $b = \begin{pmatrix} 1 \\ 2 \end{pmatrix}$. $\overrightarrow{OQ} = 2a$, $\overrightarrow{QR} = 3b$. Draw $\overrightarrow{OQ}$, $\overrightarrow{QR}$ and $\overrightarrow{OR}$. (a) Write down $\overrightarrow{OR}$ (i) as a column vector (ii) in terms of a and b. (b) Write $\overrightarrow{RQ}$ as a column vector.

2) $c = \begin{pmatrix} 1 \\ -1 \end{pmatrix}$, $d = \begin{pmatrix} 2 \\ 1 \end{pmatrix}$. $\overrightarrow{KL} = 3c$, $\overrightarrow{KM} = 2d$. Draw $\overrightarrow{KL}$, $\overrightarrow{KM}$ and $\overrightarrow{LM}$. (a) Write $\overrightarrow{LM}$ as a column vector. (b) Which of the three vectors is the resultant vector? (c) Write $\overrightarrow{LM}$ in terms of c and d.

3) $a = \begin{pmatrix} 2 \\ 3 \end{pmatrix}$, $b = \begin{pmatrix} 2 \\ -2 \end{pmatrix}$. $\overrightarrow{OT} = a$, $\overrightarrow{TU} = 2b$, $\overrightarrow{UV} = -2a$ Draw $\overrightarrow{OT}$, $\overrightarrow{TU}$, $\overrightarrow{UV}$ and $\overrightarrow{OV}$. (i) Write $\overrightarrow{OV}$ as a column vector. (ii) Write $\overrightarrow{OV}$ in terms of a and b. (iii) Write $\overrightarrow{OU}$ in terms of a and b.

4) $\overrightarrow{PQ} = \begin{pmatrix} 3 \\ 3 \end{pmatrix}$, $\overrightarrow{PR} = \begin{pmatrix} 4 \\ -4 \end{pmatrix}$. If $a = \begin{pmatrix} 1 \\ 1 \end{pmatrix}$, $b = \begin{pmatrix} 1 \\ -1 \end{pmatrix}$, express $\overrightarrow{PQ}$, $\overrightarrow{PR}$ and $\overrightarrow{QR}$ in terms of a and b.

5) $a = \begin{pmatrix} 1 \\ 3 \end{pmatrix}$, $b = \begin{pmatrix} 2 \\ 1 \end{pmatrix}$. Draw $\overrightarrow{FH} = a$, $\overrightarrow{FG} = -2b$, $\overrightarrow{GJ} = 2a$.

(a) Write $\overrightarrow{JH}$ (i) as a column vector (ii) in terms of a and b.
(b) Write $\overrightarrow{FJ}$ (i) as a column vector (ii) in terms of a and b.

---

**b**

1) Find the magnitude of each of these vectors. Answers may be left as square roots or given correct to 2 significant figures.

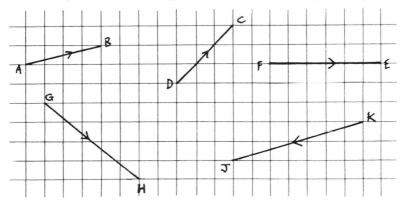

2) $a = \begin{pmatrix} 4 \\ 1 \end{pmatrix}$, $b = \begin{pmatrix} 3 \\ 3 \end{pmatrix}$. On squared paper, draw $\overrightarrow{PS} = b$, $\overrightarrow{SR} = b$, $\overrightarrow{PQ} = 2a$. Then work out the magnitude of $\overrightarrow{PS}$, $\overrightarrow{PR}$, $\overrightarrow{PQ}$, $\overrightarrow{SQ}$ and $\overrightarrow{RQ}$. Answers may be left as square roots or given correct to 2 significant figures.

# A MULTIPLICATION OF TWO BRACKETS

When two brackets are multiplied out, everything in the first bracket must be multiplied by everything in the second bracket,

e.g. Multiply out $(x + 2) (x - 3)$

| | | | |
|---|---|---|---|
| **F**irsts | $(\underline{x} + 2) (\underline{x} - 3)$ | x X x | $= x^2$ |
| **O**utsides | $(\underline{x} + 2) (x \underline{-3})$ | x X -3 | $= -3x$ |
| **I**nsides | $(x + \underline{2}) (\underline{x} - 3)$ | 2 X x | $= + 2x$ |
| **L**asts | $(x + \underline{2}) (x \underline{-3})$ | 2 X -3 | $= -6$ |

$$x^2 - 3x + 2x - 6$$
$$= \quad x^2 - x - 6$$

The answer is an expression with three terms and is called a TRINOMIAL.

---

e.g. (2) $(x + 4) (2x + 1)$

$$x \text{ X } 2x = 2x^2$$
$$x \text{ X } 1 = + x$$
$$4 \text{ X } 2x = + 8x$$
$$4 \text{ X } 1 = + 4$$
$$\overline{2x^2 + x + 8x + 4}$$
$$= \quad 2x^2 + 9x + 4$$

It is usual to write the terms in DESCENDING POWERS - **first** $x^2$ terms, **then** x terms, **then** ordinary numbers

---

e.g. (3) $(x - 5)^2 = (x - 5)(x - 5) = x^2 - 5x - 5x + 25$
$$= \quad x^2 - 10x + 25$$

e.g. (4) $2(3x + 1)(x - 4) = 2(3x^2 - 11x - 4) = 6x^2 - 22x - 8$

e.g. (5) $(x - 2y)(2x - y) = 2x^2 - xy - 4xy + 2y^2$
$$= \quad 2x^2 - 5xy + 2y^2$$

e.g. (6) $(4 + 7)(1 + 5) = 4 + 20 + 7 + 35 = 66$

e.g. (7) $(x + 3)(x - 3) = x^2 - 3x + 3x - 9 = x^2 - 9$

Example (7) is called the DIFFERENCE OF TWO SQUARES (x squared subtract 9 squared).

**a**  Multiply out
1) $(x + 3)(x + 4)$
2) $(x + 1)(x + 5)$
3) $(x + 6)(x + 2)$
4) $(x + 3)(x - 2)$
5) $(x - 5)(x + 5)$
6) $(x + 8)(x + 1)$
7) $(x - 4)(x - 2)$
8) $(x + 7)(x - 3)$
9) $(x + 4)(x + 4)$
10) $(x - 5)(x - 6)$

**b**  Multiply out
1) $(x - 12)(x - 1)$
2) $(2x + 3)(x + 2)$
3) $(x + 5)(x + 8)$
4) $(3x + 1)(x - 1)$
5) $(x - 7)(x - 4)$
6) $(x + \frac{1}{2})(x + \frac{1}{2})$
7) $(2x + 1)(2x + 2)$
8) $(x - 3)(3x - 1)$
9) $(6 + 2)(4 + 3)$
10) $(4x + 1)(2x - 5)$

**c**  Multiply out
1) $(x + 5)^2$
2) $(x - 2)^2$
3) $(x + 4)^2$
4) $(x + 3)^2$
5) $(x + y)^2$
6) $(x - y)^2$
7) $(x - 6)^2$
8) $(2x + 3)^2$
9) $(x - 9)^2$
10) $(3x + 4)^2$

**d**  Multiply out
1) $(x + 2)(x - 2)$
2) $(x + 4)(x - 4)$
3) $(x + y)(x - y)$
4) $(x + 6)(x - 6)$
5) $(x - 10)(x + 10)$
6) $(2x + 1)(2x - 1)$
7) $(x + 7)(x - 7)$
8) $(3x + 2)(3x - 2)$
9) $(7 + 3)(7 - 3)$
10) $(5x - 8)(5x + 8)$

**e**  Multiply out
1) $2(x - 1)(x + 3)$
2) $4(x + 2)(x + 4)$
3) $3(2x - 1)(x + 2)$
4) $6(x - 2)(x - 3)$
5) $4(x + y)(x + y)$
6) $5(x + 1)(x + 5)$
7) $2(x + 3)(3x - 4)$
8) $8(x - 2)(x - 1)$
9) $3(2x - 3)(2x + 3)$
10) $\frac{1}{2}(x - 6)(2x - 4)$

#  FACTORISATION (1)

## Factorising trinomials

When a trinomial of the type $Ax^2 + Bx + C$ is factorised, the result is the product of two brackets, e.g.

$$x^2 + 7x + 10 = (x + 2)(x + 5)$$

This is the opposite operation to Multiplication of Two Brackets on page 32.

* 1) Look at signs

| | | | |
|---|---|---|---|
| $x^2 + Bx + C$ | will give | $(x + \quad)$ | $(x + \quad)$ |
| $x^2 - Bx + C$ | will give | $(x - \quad)$ | $(x - \quad)$ |
| $x^2 + Bx - C$ ⎱ | will give either | $(x + \quad)$ | $(x - \quad)$ |
| and $x^2 - Bx - C$ ⎰ | or | $(x - \quad)$ | $(x + \quad)$ |

* 2) To find the second number in each bracket if the last term is +, e.g. $x^2 + 7x + 12$, find the **factors** of the last term which **ADD** to give the coefficient of the middle term.

$$x^2 \quad + 7x \quad + 12 = (x + 4)(x + 3)$$
$$\quad \quad (4 + 3) \quad (4 \times 3)$$

e.g. $a^2 \quad - 9a \quad + 14 = (a - 7)(a - 2)$

$$\quad \quad (7 + 2) \quad (7 \times 2)$$

To find the second number in each bracket if the last term is –, e.g. $x^2 + 4x - 12$, find the **factors** of the last term which **SUBTRACT** to give the coefficient of the middle term.

e.g. * $x^2 \quad + 4x \quad - 12 = (x + 6)(x - 2)$

$$\quad (6 - 2) \quad (6 \times 2)$$

* $x^2 \quad - 4x \quad - 12 = (x - 6)(x + 2)$

$$\quad (6 - 2) \quad (6 \times 2)$$

* Notice the different answers given by these two examples. If the original middle term is +, the larger number in brackets is +, e.g.

$$n^2 + 2n - 15 = (n + 5)(n - 3)$$

If the original middle term is –, the larger number in brackets is –, e.g.

$$n^2 - 2n - 15 = (n - 5)(n + 3)$$

---

**B** When factorising, always find the highest factor common to all terms first, e.g. Factorise $2x^2 - 6x - 20$

All the terms divide by 2, so take the factor of 2 out first, and then continue as before.

$$2x^2 - 6x - 20$$
$$2(x^2 - 3x - 10)$$
$$2(x - 5)(x + 2)$$

## a Factorise into two brackets

1) $x^2 + 5x + 6$
2) $x^2 + 7x + 6$
3) $x^2 + 2x + 1$
4) $p^2 + 10p + 16$
5) $c^2 + 11c + 18$
6) $x^2 + 9x + 20$
7) $y^2 + 4y + 4$
8) $x^2 - 5x + 4$
9) $m^2 - 7m + 10$
10) $x^2 - 2x + 1$
11) $x^2 - 5x + 6$
12) $a^2 - 10a + 21$
13) $x^2 + 8x + 16$
14) $h^2 + 6h + 8$
15) $x^2 - 13x + 12$

## b Factorise into two brackets

1) $x^2 + x - 2$
2) $x^2 - 3x - 18$
3) $x^2 + 8x - 9$
4) $x^2 - 6x + 9$
5) $x^2 - 4x - 5$
6) $x^2 - 10x + 25$
7) $x^2 + x - 6$
8) $x^2 + 11x + 28$
9) $x^2 - 12x + 11$
10) $x^2 + 5x - 24$
11) $x^2 + 8x + 12$
12) $x^2 - 5x - 14$
13) $x^2 + 2x - 3$
14) $x^2 - 9x + 14$
15) $x^2 + x - 20$

## c Factorise into two brackets

1) $x^2 + 25x + 24$
2) $x^2 - 18x + 80$
3) $x^2 - 20x + 100$
4) $x^2 + 2xy + y^2$
5) $x^2 - 14x - 32$
6) $x^2 + x + \frac{1}{4}$
7) $x^2 + 18x + 45$
8) $25 + 60 + 36$
9) $x^2 + 2x - 8$
10) $x^2 - 6x - 7$
11) $x^2 + 19x + 60$
12) $x^2 + 8x - 33$
13) $49 - 42 + 9$
14) $2x^2 + 3x + 1$
15) $10x^2 + 41x + 40$

## d Factorise. In each example, first find the highest factor common to all the terms. Then factorise into brackets.

1) $3x^2 + 15x + 18$
2) $2x^2 + 4x - 30$
3) $7x^2 - 7x - 14$
4) $4x^2 + 28x + 48$
5) $2x^2 - 10x + 8$
6) $5x^2 + 10x + 5$
7) $6x^2 - 30x - 84$
8) $4x^2 - 26x + 12$
9) $x^3 + 6x^2 + 5x$
10) $3x^2 + 27x - 30$

# A FACTORISATION (2)

## Difference of two squares

\* The difference of two squares is factorised as

*square root of first square + square root of second square*

multiplied by

*square root of first square − square root of second square*

e.g.
$$x^2 - y^2 = (x + y)(x - y)$$
$$n^2 - 9 = (n + 3)(n - 3)$$
$$4a^2 - 25b^2 = (2a + 5b)(2a - 5b)$$

---

# B This method can be used for problems without letters

e.g.
$$81 - 16 = (9 + 4)(9 - 4) = 13 \times 5 = 65$$
$$100^2 - 99^2 = (100 + 99)(100 - 99) = 199 \times 1 = 199$$
$$(22.6)^2 - (17.4)^2 = (22.6 + 17.4)(22.6 - 17.4) = 40 \times 5.2 = 208$$

---

# C When factorising, always find any factors common to both terms first

e.g. (1) Factorise
$$8x^2 - 2y^2$$
$$2(4x^2 - y^2)$$
$$2(2x + y)(2x - y)$$

e.g. (2) Factorise
$$27p^2 - 12q^2$$
$$3(9p^2 - 4q^2)$$
$$3(3p + 2q)(3p - 2q)$$

---

# D Factorising expressions with four terms

\*First split into two groups of two terms. Then take out common factors, e.g.
$$bd - be + cd - ce$$
$$bd - be \qquad + cd - ce$$
$$b(d - e) \qquad + c(d - e)$$
$$(b + c)(d - e)$$

Sometimes the terms need to be rearranged first,
e.g. (2)
$$uv + xy + uy + xv$$
$$uv + uy \qquad + xv + xy$$
$$u(v + y) \qquad + x(v + y)$$
$$(u + x)(v + y)$$

e.g. (3)
$$fh + gj - gh - fj$$
$$fh - fj \qquad - gh + gj$$
$$f(h - j) \qquad -g(h - j)$$
$$(f - g)(h - j)$$

**a** Multiply out these brackets (See page 32). Each answer should be a difference of two squares.

1) $(a + b)(a - b)$
2) $(x + 2)(x - 2)$
3) $(4 + y)(4 - y)$
4) $(2x + y)(2x - y)$
5) $(n - 6)(n + 6)$
6) $(5 + 2)(5 - 2)$
7) $(3a - 4b)(3a + 4b)$
8) $(6j + h)(6j - h)$
9) $(2m + 7k)(2m - 7k)$
10) $(x^2 + y)(x^2 - y)$

**b** Factorise

1) $a^2 - b^2$
2) $x^2 - 4$
3) $9h^2 - j^2$
4) $49 - 36$
5) $64x^2 - 25y^2$
6) $16a^2 - 9b^2$
7) $n^2 - \frac{4}{9}$
8) $144 - 121$
9) $x^6 - 81$
10) $4c^2 - 1$

**c** Factorise by finding common factors first

1) $2x^2 - 2y^2$
2) $3p^2 - 3q^2$
3) $2m^2 - 8t^2$
4) $18w^2 - 2v^2$
5) $2y^2 - 32$
6) $12d^2 - 27e^2$
7) $75 - 3h^2$
8) $20p^2 - 45n^2$
9) $6j^2 - 24m^2$
10) $8a^2 - 50$

**d** Find answers to these by factorising the difference of two squares

1) $59^2 - 58^2$
2) $34^2 - 24^2$
3) $201^2 - 199^2$
4) $22^2 - 17^2$
5) $89^2 - 79^2$
6) $19^2 - 16^2$
7) $148^2 - 48^2$
8) $67^2 - 63^2$
9) $59^2 - 41^2$
10) $228^2 - 222^2$
11) $(0.6)^2 - (0.4)^2$
12) $(7.2)^2 - (2.8)^2$
13) $(3.37)^2 - (1.63)^2$
14) $(9.1)^2 - (8.1)^2$
15) $(0.57)^2 - (0.43)^2$

**e** Factorise each of these into two brackets

1) $ax + ay + bx + by$
2) $cd + gd + ce + ge$
3) $ah - aj + bh - bj$
4) $mp + qn + mn + qp$
5) $st + su + ut + u^2$
6) $km - zw - kw + zm$
7) $2a + bc + ba + 2c$
8) $df - ph + pf - dh$
9) $4xy - 4xz + wy - wz$
10) $cs + pm - ps - cm$

# A QUADRATIC EQUATIONS

A QUADRATIC EQUATION is an equation containing a SQUARED term e.g. $x^2 - x - 6 = 0$

There are usually two possible values for the letter.

**To solve a quadratic equation**    e.g. $x^2 - x - 6 = 0$

* 1) Factorise                                        $(x - 3)(x + 2) = 0$

* 2) When the two brackets are multiplied,
they make zero, so one of the                         $x - 3 = 0$
brackets must equal zero                        or    $x + 2 = 0$

　　　　　　so the solution is    $x = 3$  or  $x = -2$

e.g. (2)                          e.g. (3)

$x^2 - 9x + 20 = 0$                $2x^2 - 5x - 12 = 0$

$(x - 5)(x - 4) = 0$              $(x - 4)(2x + 3) = 0$

$x = 5$  or  $x = 4$              $x = 4$  or  $x = -1\frac{1}{2}$

---

# B

If the expression to be factorised does not equal 0, change the equation to obtain 0 on the right–hand side, e.g

$$x^2 + 2x = 63$$
$$x^2 + 2x - 63 = 0$$
$$(x + 9)(x - 7) = 0$$
$$\underline{x = -9}  \text{ or }  \underline{x = 7}$$

---

# C Using the formula

If a quadratic equation cannot be solved by the method shown in A at the top of this page, the formula can be used.

For the quadratic equation $Ax^2 + Bx + C = 0$

$$x = \frac{-B \pm \sqrt{B^2 - 4AC}}{2A}$$

e.g. Solve the quadratic equation $3x^2 + 4x - 5 = 0$ giving your answer correct to 2 decimal places.

$$(+3)x^2 (+4)x (-5) = 0$$
$$A = 3 , \quad B = 4 , \quad C = -5$$

so

$$x = \frac{-4 \pm \sqrt{4^2 - (4 \times 3 \times -5)}}{2 \times 3}$$

$$x = \frac{-4 + \sqrt{76}}{6} \qquad\qquad x = \frac{-4 - \sqrt{76}}{6}$$

$$\underline{x = 0.79}  \text{ or }  \underline{x = -2.12}  \text{ (2d.p.)}$$

**a** Find the possible values of x in each of these

1) $(x - 1)(x - 2) = 0$
2) $(x - 5)(x + 1) = 0$
3) $(x + 3)(x + 6) = 0$
4) $(x - 8)(x - 4) = 0$
5) $(x + 11)(x - 3) = 0$

6) $(2x - 3)(x - 1) = 0$
7) $(x + 5)(3x - 2) = 0$
8) $(x - 9)(x + 6) = 0$
9) $(4x + 5)(2x - 7) = 0$
10) $(x - 8)(4x - 1) = 0$

**b** Solve these quadratic equations

1) $x^2 - 5x + 6 = 0$
2) $x^2 - 6x + 5 = 0$
3) $x^2 + 2x - 3 = 0$
4) $x^2 + 12x + 35 = 0$
5) $x^2 + x - 12 = 0$
6) $x^2 - 9x + 14 = 0$
7) $x^2 - 2x + 1 = 0$
8) $x^2 + 8x + 7 = 0$

9) $x^2 - 13x + 36 = 0$
10) $x^2 - 2x - 48 = 0$
11) $x^2 - 26x + 48 = 0$
12) $x^2 + 2x - 15 = 0$
13) $x^2 - 8x - 20 = 0$
14) $x^2 + 11x + 28 = 0$
15) $x^2 - 9x + 20 = 0$

**c** Solve these quadratic equations

1) $2x^2 - 11x + 12 = 0$
2) $3x^2 + 10x - 8 = 0$
3) $x^2 + 24x - 25 = 0$
4) $2x^2 + 17x + 8 = 0$
5) $x^2 - 4x - 32 = 0$

6) $x^2 - 7x + 6 = 0$
7) $x^2 - 15x + 54 = 0$
8) $2x^2 - 9x + 7 = 0$
9) $x^2 + 2x - 63 = 0$
10) $3x^2 + 8x + 4 = 0$

**d** Solve these quadratic equations. Rearrange each one first so that it is in the form $Ax^2 \pm Bx \pm C = 0$

1) $x^2 + 3x = 18$
2) $x^2 - 8x = 20$
3) $x^2 - 9x = -20$
4) $x^2 + 4x = 12$
5) $x^2 + x = 6$

6) $x^2 + 9x = 36$
7) $x^2 - 4x = 21$
8) $2x^2 - x = 1$
9) $x^2 - 8x = -16$
10) $x^2 - x = 42$

**e** Solve these quadratic equations using the formula on page 38 **C**. Give answers to 2 decimal places. Square roots can be looked up on page 71.

1) $x^2 + 5x - 2 = 0$
2) $2x^2 - 4x + 1 = 0$
3) $x^2 + 2x - 6 = 0$
4) $3x^2 - 4x - 2 = 0$
5) $x^2 - 7x + 3 = 0$

6) $2x^2 + 5x + 3 = 0$
7) $5x^2 - 10x + 4 = 0$
8) $8x^2 - 14x - 9 = 0$
9) $2x^2 + 6x - 5 = 0$
10) $4x^2 - 7x = 1$

# A PROBABILITY

Probability is the likelihood that something (called an EVENT) will happen. It is expressed as a quantity between 0 and 1 inclusive. If an event will definitely happen, the probability is 1, e.g. the probability that the month after next April will be next May is 1. If an event will definitely not happen, the probability is 0, e.g. the probability that the Pacific Ocean will dry up today is 0.

If an event is just as likely to happen as not to happen, the probability is $\frac{1}{2}$ (or 0.5), e.g. the probability of a coin landing heads up when I toss it is $\frac{1}{2}$.

Probability is written as either 0, 1, or a fraction or decimal between 0 and 1. If it is written as a fraction, it should be cancelled to its lowest terms.

# B

The way that an event **does** happen, or the way you wish it to happen is called a SUCCESSFUL (or FAVOURABLE) OUTCOME. The number of ways an event can happen is called the SAMPLE SPACE.

$$\text{Probability} = \frac{\text{Number of successful outcomes}}{\text{Sample space}}$$

e.g. The probability that a die will fall with ⚁ upwards is $\frac{1}{6}$ because there are 6 different ways the die **can** fall and only 1 way it **does** fall.

e.g. (2) The probability of picking an ace out of a well-shuffled pack of cards is $\frac{4}{52} = \frac{1}{13}$ because there are 52 different cards which can be picked but only 4 which are the kind required.

No. of successful outcomes = No. of aces = 4
Sample space = No. of cards = 52
Probability (ace) = $\frac{4}{52} = \frac{1}{13}$

If the ace that has been picked is kept out of the pack, what is the probability of picking another ace? Now the sample space is 51 (because there are now only 51 cards left in the pack) and the number of successful outcomes is 3 (because there are now only 3 aces in the pack) so the probability is $\frac{3}{51} = \frac{1}{17}$

# C Events not happening

The probability of an event **not** happening is found by subtracting the probability of its happening from 1, e.g. the probability of a die falling with the ⚀ upwards is $\frac{1}{6}$, so the probability of its **not** falling with the ⚀ upwards is

$$1 - \frac{1}{6} = \frac{5}{6}$$

**a**

1) Find the probability
   (a) when a die is thrown, that the number facing upwards will be divisible by 3
   (b) when a card is picked from a pack, it will be a 'diamond'
   (c) of the name of a month beginning with a letter A
   (d) that I shall meet a live dinosaur tomorrow
   (e) that, if I cut out the letters of the word LOLLIPOP, and mix them up in a box, I shall pick a letter L out of the box

2) A red die and a green die are thrown together. Copy and complete this table to find all the different combinations of score

| RED DIE | | | 1 | 1 | | |
|---|---|---|---|---|---|---|
| GREEN DIE | | | 1 | 2 | | |
| TOTAL SCORE (red + green) | | | 2 | 3 | | etc. |

3) From your answer to question 2, find the probability that the total score will be
   (i) 5   (ii) 11   (iii) 1   (iv) 7   (v) 4

4) (i) If two coins are tossed, what is the probability of both coins landing heads up?
   (ii) What is the probability of the coins landing with one head and one tail facing upwards?

5) There are 10 red sweets, 8 yellow sweets and 7 green sweets in a bag
   (a) What is the sample space (the total number of sweets)?
   (b) If I dip into the bag without looking, what is the probability of picking a red sweet?
   (c) If I eat the red sweet I have picked, what is now the probability that I shall pick a yellow sweet?

6) When a football team plays a match, the result is either win, lose or draw. Assuming all results to be equally likely, find the probability that
   (a) a single match will be a draw
   (b) a single match will not be a draw
   (c) two matches will both result in a draw
   (d) three matches will all result in a draw

7) (a) Three coins are tossed together. Copy and complete this table to find all the different ways (the sample space) the coins can land (H=heads, T=tails)

| COIN 1 | H | H | | |
|---|---|---|---|---|
| COIN 2 | H | H | | |
| COIN 3 | H | T | | etc. |

   (b) From your answer to (a) find
      (i) the probability of all three coins landing tails up
      (ii) the probability of the coins landing with one head and two tails
   (c) Without listing all the possibilities, try to work out the probability of four coins all landing heads up when they are tossed together.

# A MEAN, MODE, MEDIAN & RANGE

## Mean

The correct name is 'arithmetic mean'. Mean is often called 'average'. The mean is calculated by adding together all the quantities (or amounts) and dividing the total by how many quantities (or amounts) there are, e.g. in this group of 30 numbers

| 3 | 9 | 7 | 0 | 7 | 1 | 5 | 2 | 3 | 8 | 6 | 4 | 5 | 8 | 6 |
| 0 | 4 | 9 | 7 | 1 | 3 | 6 | 2 | 1 | 8 | 5 | 0 | 4 | 8 | 3 |

the total of the numbers is 135, so the mean is

$$\frac{135}{30} = 4\tfrac{1}{2}$$

## B Mode

The mode (or modal value) of a group of quantities is the quantity which occurs, or happens, most often in the group, e.g. in this group

| 69 | 72 | 75 | 68 | 62 | 70 | 63 | 68 | 66 |
| 71 | 68 | 64 | 73 | 70 | 69 | 59 | 67 | 71 |

the mode is 68 because it occurs more often than any other number.

## C Median

If a group of quantities is listed in order of size, the median is the middle quantity in the list, e.g. to find the median of

| 17 | 22 | 23 | 16 | 24 | 20 | 16 | 23 | 19 | 21 | 26 |

arrange in order of size

| 16 | 16 | 17 | 19 | 20 | 21 | 22 | 23 | 23 | 24 | 26 |

The median is 21 because it is the middle quantity.

If the group contains an EVEN number of quantities, the median is half–way between the middle quantities (or the mean of the two middle quantities), e.g. to find the median of

| 42 | 48 | 41 | 44 | 47 | 49 |,

arrange in order of size        41    42    44    47    48    49
The median is $45\tfrac{1}{2}$ (half–way between 44 and 47, or the mean of 44 and 47).

## D Range

The range of a group of quantities is found by subtracting the smallest quantity from the largest, e.g.

in the group        83    82    87    84    92    88    78    80

the range is              92 − 78 = 14

**a** Find the mean of each group of numbers
1) 53, 55, 49, 57, 63, 52, 59, 60
2) 20, 18, 26, 32, 15, 42, 25, 16, 28, 19, 23
3) 4, 12, 7, 8, 6, 2, 5, 11, 5, 16, 6, 9, 7, 10, 8, 4
4) 35, 27, 35, 47, 29, 40, 37, 36, 38
5) 6, 4, 3, 7, 8, 5, 3, 7, 2, 3, 3, 8, 9, 4, 1, 5, 6, 6, 3, 2

---

**b** Find the mode of each group
1) 7, 5, 3, 6, 1, 8, 6, 7, 3, 9, 4, 5, 6, 2, 9, 4
2) 8, 5, 6, 5, 7, 8, 5, 4, 7, 5, 6, 8, 5, 6
3) 72, 75, 71, 73, 68, 69, 79, 73, 71, 71, 74, 69, 73, 67, 73, 76
4) B, A, S, E, B, A, L, L, M, A, T, C, H, E, S
5) 44, 43, 41, 47, 45, 43, 47, 41, 47
   44, 46, 41, 44, 47, 48, 42, 40, 43

---

**c** Find the median of each group of numbers
1) 42, 48, 54, 43, 56, 52, 41, 47, 48, 52, 49, 45, 50
2) 4, 2, 3, 6, 8, 5, 7, 9, 2, 5, 4, 1, 3, 7, 8, 4, 1
3) 123, 118, 127, 133, 128, 122, 128, 119, 130, 121
4) 18, 15, 16, 25, 13, 19, 30, 22, 27, 16, 33, 22, 17, 24, 14
5) 77, 82, 78, 77, 79, 82, 78, 80, 77
   79, 83, 81, 82, 78, 77, 81, 80, 81

---

**d** For each of these groups of numbers, work out
(a) the mean, (b) the mode, (c) the median, (d) the range

1)
| 5 | 7 | 8 | 7 | 4 | 6 | 1 | 2 | 4 | 7 |
|---|---|---|---|---|---|---|---|---|---|
| 4 | 9 | 4 | 6 | 1 | 8 | 2 | 6 | 8 | 1 |

2)
| 24 | 28 | 23 | 24 | 34 | 27 | 24 | 26 | 24 | 29 |
|----|----|----|----|----|----|----|----|----|----|
| 25 | 21 | 28 | 30 | 25 | 27 | 29 | 19 | 28 | 27 |
| 25 | 27 | 24 | 32 | 20 |    |    |    |    |    |

3)
| 94 | 72 | 58 | 85 | 61 | 54 | 80 | 56 | 74 | 66 |
|----|----|----|----|----|----|----|----|----|----|

4)
| 12 | 17 | 16 | 20 | 14 | 9 | 22 | 15 | 16 | 20 |
|----|----|----|----|----|---|----|----|----|----|
| 17 | 12 | 21 | 19 | 16 | 10 | 15 | 12 | 21 | 11 |
| 16 | 20 | 10 | 24 | 9 | 21 | 8 | 16 | 23 | 18 |

5)
| 6 | 10 | 4 | 12 | 7 | 5 | 12 | 3 | 11 | 3 | 15 | 8 |
|---|----|---|----|---|---|----|---|----|---|----|---|
| 9 | 2 | 10 | 9 | 4 | 11 | 6 | 12 | 16 | 5 | 9 | 13 |
| 3 | 1 | 9 | 11 | 8 | 2 | 7 | 19 | 10 | 4 | 14 | 7 |

# A TRIGONOMETRY (1)

Trigonometry means 'measuring three–cornered figures'. It shows the connection (or relationship) between the angles and the sides of a triangle.

This book shows only the simplest kind of trigonometry using SINE (sin), COSINE (cos), and TANGENT (tan).

# B Right-angled triangle

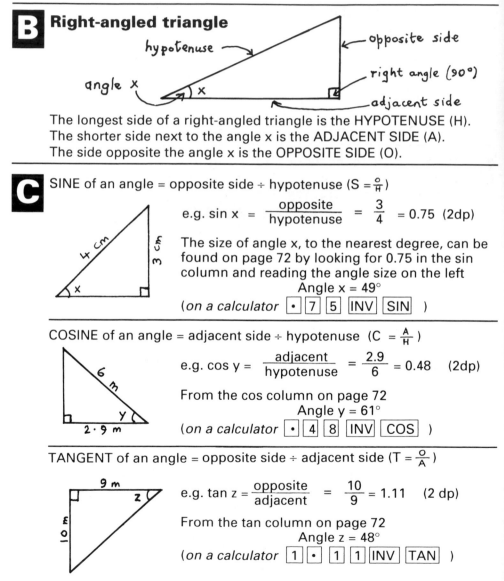

The longest side of a right-angled triangle is the HYPOTENUSE (H).
The shorter side next to the angle x is the ADJACENT SIDE (A).
The side opposite the angle x is the OPPOSITE SIDE (O).

# C

SINE of an angle = opposite side ÷ hypotenuse (S = $\frac{O}{H}$)

e.g. $\sin x = \dfrac{\text{opposite}}{\text{hypotenuse}} = \dfrac{3}{4} = 0.75$ (2dp)

The size of angle x, to the nearest degree, can be found on page 72 by looking for 0.75 in the sin column and reading the angle size on the left

Angle x = 49°

(*on a calculator* [·] [7] [5] [INV] [SIN] )

---

COSINE of an angle = adjacent side ÷ hypotenuse (C = $\frac{A}{H}$)

e.g. $\cos y = \dfrac{\text{adjacent}}{\text{hypotenuse}} = \dfrac{2.9}{6} = 0.48$ (2dp)

From the cos column on page 72

Angle y = 61°

(*on a calculator* [·] [4] [8] [INV] [COS] )

---

TANGENT of an angle = opposite side ÷ adjacent side (T = $\frac{O}{A}$)

e.g. $\tan z = \dfrac{\text{opposite}}{\text{adjacent}} = \dfrac{10}{9} = 1.11$ (2 dp)

From the tan column on page 72

Angle z = 48°

(*on a calculator* [1] [·] [1] [1] [INV] [TAN] )

**a** (Triangles on this page are not drawn to scale)

Work out the sines of angles a, b, c, d, e correct to 2 decimal places. Then, by looking in the sin column on page 72, write down, to the nearest degree, the size of each angle.

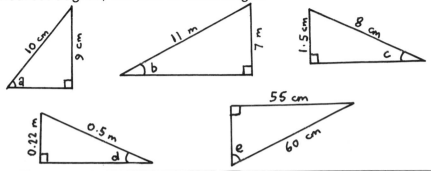

**b** Work out the cosines of angles f, g, h, j, k correct to 2 decimal places. Then, by looking in the cos column on page 72, write down, to the nearest degree, the size of each angle.

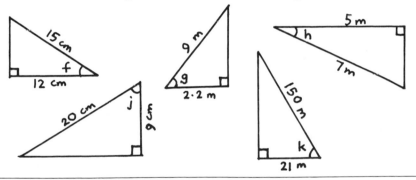

**c** Work out the tangents of angles l, m, n, p, q correct to 2 decimal places. Then, by looking in the tan column on page 72, write down, to the nearest degree, the size of each angle.

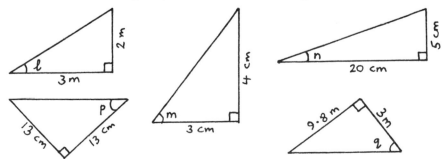

# A TRIGONOMETRY (2)

## Sine (sin)

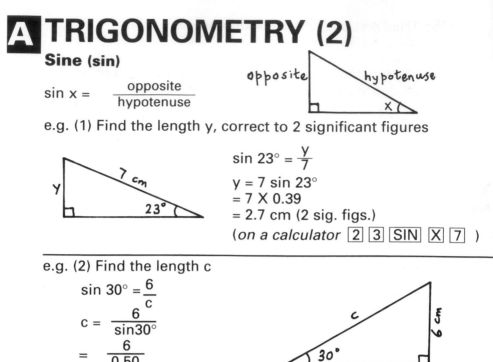

$$\sin x = \frac{\text{opposite}}{\text{hypotenuse}}$$

opposite   hypotenuse

x

e.g. (1) Find the length y, correct to 2 significant figures

$$\sin 23° = \frac{y}{7}$$

$$y = 7 \sin 23°$$

$$= 7 \times 0.39$$

$$= 2.7 \text{ cm (2 sig. figs.)}$$

(*on a calculator* [2] [3] [SIN] [X] [7] )

7 cm

y

23°

---

e.g. (2) Find the length c

$$\sin 30° = \frac{6}{c}$$

$$c = \frac{6}{\sin 30°}$$

$$= \frac{6}{0.50}$$

$$= 12 \text{ cm (2 sig. figs)}$$

c

6 cm

30°

---

e.g. (3) A straight pine tree 17 metres tall is blown over in a gale so that its top rests against a vertical building.

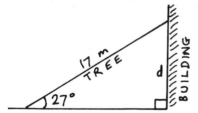

17 m TREE

d

BUILDING

27°

The ground between the foot of the tree and the base of the building is level, and the tree makes an angle of 27° with the ground. How far up the building (d) is the top of the tree?

$$\sin 27° = \frac{d}{17}$$

$$d = 17 \sin 27°$$

$$= 17 \times 0.45 = 7.7 \text{ (2 sig. figs)}$$

The top of the tree is 7.7 metres up the building

---

**REMEMBER** the short way of writing expressions in trigonometry, e.g. 3 sin 47° is short for 3 X the sine of 47°.

USE THE TABLE ON PAGE 72 OR AN ELECTRONIC CALCULATOR.
GIVE ANSWERS CORRECT TO 2 SIGNIFICANT FIGURES.

**a** Write down the value of each of these. Remember that, for example, '6 sin 51°' means '6 X the sine of 51°'.

1) sin 37°          5) sin 4°          9) 5 sin 40°
2) sin 84°          6) sin 55°         10) 2 sin 59°
3) sin 11°          7) sin 17°
4) sin 76°          8) 3 sin 27°

---

**b** Find the lengths a, b, c, d and e in these diagrams (not drawn to scale)

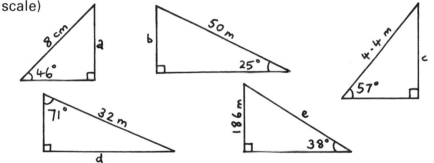

---

**c** Use sines to work these out. Make a rough drawing each time.

1) The top of a sloping plank 2.5m long just touches the top of a vertical wall. The bottom of the plank and the bottom of the wall are on level ground and the plank makes an angle of 37° with the ground. Find the height of the wall.

2) Maldon (M) is due east of Chelmsford (C). Basildon (B) is due south of Chelmsford. The distance from Basildon to Maldon is 23km and CB̂M = 40°. How far is Maldon from Chelmsford?

3) The jib of a crane is 30m long and makes an angle of 43° with the ground. Calculate the vertical height of the top of the jib.

4) The diagram shows a steep road (ST) climbing a hill from the sea shore (S). If a car is at point T, how far above sea level is it (RT)?

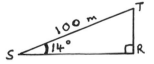

5) An aircraft attempting to fly due north is blown off course so that it follows a bearing 012°. After flying 15 km, how much further east is it than it should be?

# A TRIGONOMETRY (3)

## Cosine (cos)

$$\cos x = \frac{\text{adjacent}}{\text{hypotenuse}}$$

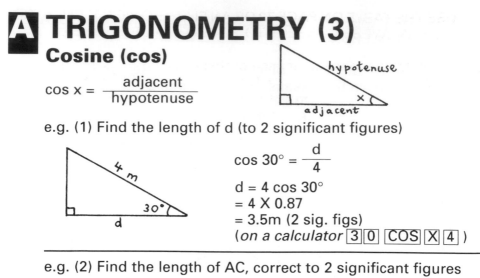

e.g. (1) Find the length of d (to 2 significant figures)

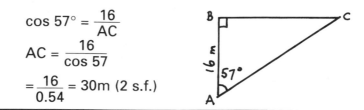

$$\cos 30° = \frac{d}{4}$$

$d = 4 \cos 30°$

$= 4 \times 0.87$

$= 3.5m$ (2 sig. figs)

(*on a calculator* [3][0] [COS][X][4] )

---

e.g. (2) Find the length of AC, correct to 2 significant figures

$$\cos 57° = \frac{16}{AC}$$

$$AC = \frac{16}{\cos 57}$$

$$= \frac{16}{0.54} = 30m \text{ (2 s.f.)}$$

---

e.g. (3) An aeroplane sets off from a landing strip (L) and flies on a bearing 130°. After it has flown 11.5km it drops supplies at a village (V). Then it changes course, heading due north on another mission, and passes over a farmstead (F) which is due east of the landing strip. How far, correct to 2 significant figures, is the farmstead from the landing strip?

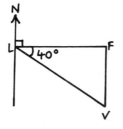

The aeroplane is flying on a bearing 130°, so angle FLV = 130–90 = 40°

$$\cos 40° = \frac{LF}{11.5}$$

$LF = 11.5 \cos 40°$

$= 11.5 \times 0.77 = 8.9$

The farmstead is 8.9km from the landing strip (2 sig. figs.)

---

NOTE. The cosine of x° has the same value as the sine of (90 – x)°,

e.g.

$\cos 29° = \sin 61° = \frac{a}{h}$

$\sin 29° = \cos 61° = \frac{b}{h}$

USE THE TABLE ON PAGE 72 OR AN ELECTRONIC CALCULATOR.
GIVE ANSWERS CORRECT TO 2 SIGNIFICANT FIGURES.

**a** Write down the value of each of these
1) cos 53°           5) cos 77°           9) 7 cos 70°
2) cos 17°           6) cos 63°           10) 3 cos 34°
3) cos 84°           7) 4 cos 82°
4) cos 41°           8) 2 cos 59°

---

**b** Find the lengths f, g, h, j and k in these diagrams (not drawn to scale)

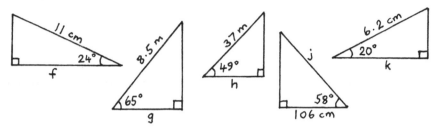

---

**c** Use cosines to work these out. Make a rough drawing each time.

1) A ladder is propped against a vertical wall with its foot on level ground 2.7m from the wall. The ladder makes an angle of 69° with the ground. How long is the ladder?

2)
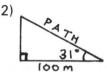
The distance from the bottom to the top of Howden Hill is shown on a map as 100m. The hill makes an angle of 31° with the level ground. How long is the path which goes from the bottom to the top of the hill?

3) From a harbour, a boat sails 6km on a bearing 145°, then changes course and sails due west until it is due south of the harbour. How far must it now sail to return to the harbour?

4) A straight road runs due west to due east. Thomas and Stephen set off from a point 2.4km due south of the road. Thomas walks due north; Stephen walks on a bearing 041°. How much further than Thomas does Stephen walk before reaching the road?

5) A piece of play apparatus consists of a flight of steps AD, 3m long, at an angle of 62° to the ground, connected at D to a slide DC, 5m long, at an angle of 32° to the ground. By calculating the lengths of AB and BC, work out the distance between the bottom of the steps and the bottom of the slide.

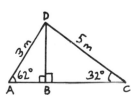

# A TRIGONOMETRY (4)

## Tangent (tan)

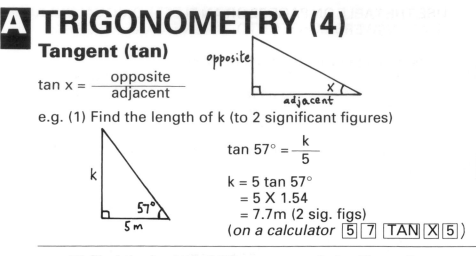

$$\tan x = \frac{\text{opposite}}{\text{adjacent}}$$

e.g. (1) Find the length of k (to 2 significant figures)

$$\tan 57° = \frac{k}{5}$$

$$k = 5 \tan 57°$$
$$= 5 \times 1.54$$
$$= 7.7\text{m (2 sig. figs)}$$

(*on a calculator* $\boxed{5}\boxed{7}$ $\boxed{\text{TAN}}\boxed{\times}\boxed{5}$ )

e.g. (2) Find the length of PQ, correct to 2 significant figures

$$\tan 31° = \frac{7}{PQ}$$

$$PQ = \frac{7}{\tan 31°} = \frac{7}{0.60} = 12\text{cm (2 sig. figs)}$$

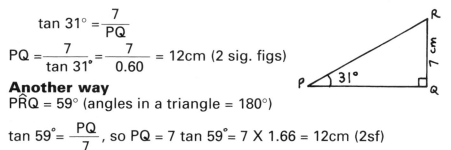

### Another way

$$P\hat{R}Q = 59° \text{ (angles in a triangle = 180°)}$$

$$\tan 59° = \frac{PQ}{7}, \text{ so } PQ = 7 \tan 59° = 7 \times 1.66 = 12\text{cm (2sf)}$$

# B Measuring heights with a clinometer

e.g. A girl stands on level ground exactly 15 metres from the foot of a vertical flagpole. She points a clinometer at the top of the flagpole and reads off an angle of 28°. What is the height (H) of the flagpole?

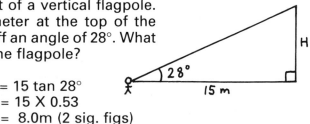

$$\tan 28° = \frac{H}{15}, \text{ so } H = 15 \tan 28°$$
$$= 15 \times 0.53$$
$$= 8.0\text{m (2 sig. figs)}$$

**NOTE** If the girl's eye is (e.g.) 1.3m above the ground when she uses the clinometer, an extra 1.3m must be added to the answer to find the correct height of the flagpole (from the ground to the top). The flagpole in this example is really 8.0 + 1.3 = 9.3 metres high (2 sig. figs)

USE THE TABLE ON PAGE 72 OR AN ELECTRONIC CALCULATOR.
GIVE ANSWERS CORRECT TO 2 SIGNIFICANT FIGURES.

## a

Write down the value of each of these
1) tan 7°      5) tan 45°      9) 5 tan 44°
2) tan 61°     6) 4 tan 63°    10) 9 tan 21°
3) tan 37°     7) 2 tan 19°
4) tan 79°     8) tan 26°

## b

Find the lengths n, p, q, r and s in these diagrams (not drawn to scale)

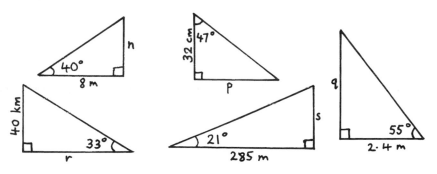

## c

Use tangents to work these out. Make a rough drawing each time.

1) A boy stands on level ground 200m from the foot of a tower and observes the top of the tower with a clinometer which shows an angle of 19°. Find the height of the tower.

2) William walks 500m due east (090°) from a pine tree (T) and stops. David walks from T on a bearing 060° until he is due north of William. How far is David from William?

3) The base (AB) of a rectangular window ABCD is 44cm long. The diagonal AC makes an angle of 60° with the base. How high is the window?

4) A helicopter is directly above a lighthouse and is hovering at 315m above sea level. An observer on a yacht points a clinometer at the helicopter and records an angle of 12°. Calculate the distance of the yacht from the lighthouse.

5) A man uses a clinometer to measure the height of a tree. He stands 20m from the tree on level ground and points the clinometer at the top of the tree. The clinometer records an angle of 25°. (a) What is the height of the tree from the man's eye? (b) If the man's eye is 1.6m above the ground, what is the correct height of the tree?

# A TRIGONOMETRY (5)

## Calculations using sine, cosine or tangent

$$\text{SINE} = \frac{\text{OPPOSITE}}{\text{HYPOTENUSE}} \quad \bigg| \quad \text{COSINE} = \frac{\text{ADJACENT}}{\text{HYPOTENUSE}} \quad \bigg| \quad \text{TANGENT} = \frac{\text{OPPOSITE}}{\text{ADJACENT}}$$

To find out which formula to use, see which sides of the triangle you either **know** or are **trying to find**, e.g. Find the length of PQ

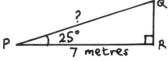

In this triangle, we **know** the length PR (ADJACENT side) and we are **trying to find** the length PQ (HYPOTENUSE), so we use the COSINE formula

$$\cos 25° = \frac{7}{PQ} \textbf{ or } PQ = \frac{7}{\cos 25°} = 7.7\text{m (1 dp)}$$

(The length QR is of no interest to us in this calculation.)
e.g. (2) Find the length d

In this triangle we **know** the ADJACENT side which is 17 cm long, and we are **trying to find** the OPPOSITE side (d).
We use the TANGENT formula

$$\tan 36° = \frac{d}{17} \textbf{ or } d = 17 \tan 36° = 12.4\text{cm (1dp)}$$

## B Angle of elevation; angle of depression

Angle of elevation is the angle which a point makes above the horizontal

e.g. TÂB is the angle of elevation of the tree top (T) from the person (A) looking at it.

angle of elevation

angle of depression

Angle of depression is the angle which a point makes below the horizontal

e.g. EĈD is the angle of depression of the dog (D) from the person (C) looking at it.

USE THE TABLE ON PAGE 72 OR AN ELECTRONIC CALCULATOR.
GIVE ANSWERS CORRECT TO 2 SIGNIFICANT FIGURES.

**a** Find the lengths a, b, c, d, e, f, g, h, j, k.

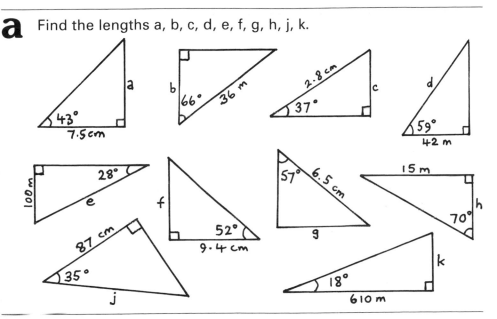

**b**

1) A boat on a horizontal sea is 90m from the top of a vertical cliff. The angle of elevation of the cliff top from the boat is 20°. How high above sea level is the cliff top?

2) A fisherman (F) and a bird watcher (B) sit 40m apart on the same bank of a straight river. A willow tree (W) grows on the other bank exactly opposite the bird watcher. Angle BF̂W is 32°. Calculate (a) the width of the river; (b) the distance between the fisherman and the willow tree.

3) 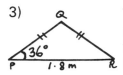 The diagram shows the cross section of the roof of a shed. The owner of the shed wishes to cover the sloping part with roofing felt. What length (PQR) of felt will be needed?

4) Amy looks out of an upstairs window of her house and observes Kate who is standing outside on level ground 10.5m from the house. The angle of depression of Kate from Amy is 24°. Find Amy's height above the ground.

5) The villages of Cantwell and Meakin Brow, which are 1.5km apart, are respectively at the bottom and top of a steady slope which makes an angle of 8° with the horizontal. Calculate, in metres, the difference in height above sea level of the two villages.

# **A** CIRCLE (1)

**Centre** of a circle is the point in the exact middle of the circle. It is nearly always given the letter O.

**Radius** of a circle is a straight line from the centre to the perimeter (circumference) of the circle. It is usually called r or R.

**Diameter** of a circle is a straight line which passes through the centre and crosses the circle from side to side. It is usually called d or D.

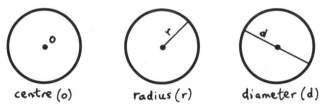

centre (o)          radius (r)          diameter (d)

The diameter is twice the length of the radius          d = 2r

---

**B** $\pi$ is a Greek letter 'pi' (pronounced like apple **pie**) which stands for a number. $\pi$ is a complicated decimal which goes on for ever but does not recur. It is roughly equal to 3.14 or $\frac{22}{7}$ and is used for many circle calculations

---

**C** **Circumference** (C) is the perimeter of a circle (all the way round the outside)

Circumference = $\pi$ X diameter

or          Circumference = 2 X $\pi$ X radius

C = 2$\pi$r

e.g. (1) ($\pi$ = 3.14) Find the circumference of a circle whose radius is 5cm.

C = 2 X 3.14 X 5
= 31.4          Circumference is 31.4cm

e.g. (2) ($\pi$ = $\frac{22}{7}$ ) Calculate the circumference of a circle with radius 28cm.

$$C = 2 \times \frac{22}{7} \times 28$$

= 176          Circumference is 176 cm

**a** Find the diameter of a circle whose radius is
1) 3cm  3) 62cm  5) 94m
2) 4.7cm  4) 25mm

**b** Find the radius of a circle whose diameter is
1) 82m  3) 14.6cm  5) 7.5 cm
2) 34cm  4) 11 miles

**c** ($\pi$ = 3.14) Calculate, correct to 2 significant figures, the circumference of a circle whose radius is
1) 1km  5) 2.4m  9) 15cm
2) 9cm  6) 3cm  10) 0.8m
3) 0.5m  7) 12cm
4) 4cm  8) 6.5m

**d** ($\pi = \frac{22}{7}$) Calculate the circumference of a circle whose radius is
1) 7cm  5) $1\frac{2}{5}$ m  9) $6\frac{3}{10}$ cm
2) 350m  6) 77cm  10) $10\frac{1}{2}$ m
3) 21cm  7) 56m
4) $\frac{1}{11}$ m  8) x cm

**e** ($\pi$ = 3.14) Give answers to 2 significant figures

1) Find the perimeter of a semicircle whose radius is 4cm

2) A bicycle has a wheel with radius 30cm. By finding the circumference of the wheel, calculate how far the bicycle travels when the wheel turns round 5 times.

3) The minute hand of a large clock is 4m long.
What distance does the tip of the hand travel in

    (a)  1 hour?

    (b)  20 minutes?

4) Find the circumference of a car steering wheel which has a diameter of 38cm

5)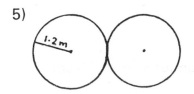

A simple model railway track is in the shape of a figure eight made out of two circles each of radius 1.2m. Calculate the complete length of the track.

# A CIRCLE (2)

## Area (A) of a circle

Area = π X radius X radius

$A = \pi r^2$

e.g. ($\pi$ = 3.14) Find the area of a circle whose radius is 15cm

A = 3.14 X 15 X 15

A = 706.5                    <u>Area is 706.5 cm²</u>

e.g. (2)    ($\pi = \frac{22}{7}$) Calculate the area of a circle whose radius is 21m

$A = \frac{22}{7} X \frac{21}{1} X \frac{21}{1}$

A = 1386                    <u>Area is 1386m²</u>

e.g. (3) ($\pi$ = 3.14) A semicircle has a radius of 3cm. What is its area, correct to 3 significant figures?

Area of semicircle = $\frac{1}{2}(\pi r^2)$

A = $\frac{1}{2}$ (3.14 X 3 X 3)

A = 14.13                    <u>Area is 14.1cm²</u>
(3 sig. figs.)

---

# B Area of an annulus

An annulus is a ring formed by two concentric circles.

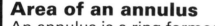
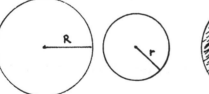
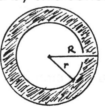

Radius of large circle is R

Radius of small circle is r

Area of annulus =
area of large circle – area of small circle

$A = \pi R^2 - \pi r^2$

or    $A = \pi(R^2 - r^2)$

e.g. ($\pi$ = 3.14) Find the area between two concentric circles whose radii are 6cm and 4cm

A = 3.14(6² – 4²)

= 3.14(36 – 16)

= 3.14 X 20

= 62.8                    <u>Area is 62.8cm²</u>

NOTE. (R² – r²) is the DIFFERENCE OF TWO SQUARES (see page 36). It could sometimes be easier to factorise first and use

$A = \pi(R + r)(R - r)$

Give answers correct to 2 significant figures, except in part b where exact answers should be given.

**a** ($\pi = 3.14$) Find the area of a circle whose radius is

| | | |
|---|---|---|
| 1) 2cm | 5) 3m | 9) k metres |
| 2) 5cm | 6) 9cm | 10) 3.2m |
| 3) 0.4m | 7) 8.3cm | |
| 4) 10cm | 8) 55cm | |

**b** ($\pi = \frac{22}{7}$) Find the area of a circle whose radius is

| | | |
|---|---|---|
| 1) 14cm | 5) 4cm | 9) $\frac{7}{11}$cm |
| 2) 35cm | 6) $\frac{1}{2}$km | 10) y cm |
| 3) 0.7m | 7) 42m | |
| 4) 2.8m | 8) 77cm | |

**c** ($\pi = 3.14$) Find the area of a semicircle whose radius is

| | | |
|---|---|---|
| 1) 6cm | 3) 0.8m | 5) 66m |
| 2) 1.6m | 4) 13cm | |

**d** ($\pi = 3.14$) Find the area of an annulus with
1) outer radius 5cm , inner radius 3cm
2) outer radius 10cm, inner radius 8cm
3) outer radius 1.5m, inner radius 0.6m
4) outer radius 13cm, inner radius 5cm
5) outer radius 25cm, inner radius 24cm

**e** ($\pi = 3.14$)

1) Find the area of a circular archery target which has a radius of 40cm.

2) A circular road-roundabout with radius 7m contains a circular flower bed with radius 5m. The rest of the roundabout is covered with grass. Calculate the grass-covered area.

3) The front of a bird nesting box is made of a piece of wood in the shape of a rectangle 19cm high and 13cm wide. A circular hole with radius 1.5cm is cut out. What area of wood remains?

4)  A door is in the shape of a rectangle 1.2m wide and 1.7m high surmounted by a semicircle as shown in the diagram. Find the total area of the door.

5) A circular goldfish pond with radius 3m is surrounded by a stone path 1m wide. Calculate (a) the area of the pond, (b) the area of the path.

#  CIRCLE (3)

A **CHORD** is a straight line joining two points on the circumference of a circle.
A **SEGMENT** is one of the regions of a circle formed when the circle is cut by a chord.
An **ARC** is part of the circumference of a circle.

##  Angles in the SAME SEGMENT of a circle are EQUAL
e.g.

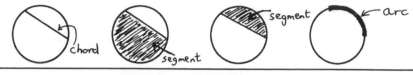

AĈB, AD̂B, AÊB, AF̂B, and AĜB are all EQUAL.
They all 'stand' on AB with their 'feet' at A and B. They are all in the same segment of the circle.

## Angles in a SEMICIRCLE are RIGHT ANGLES

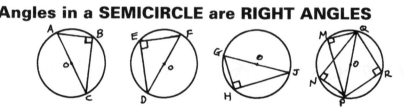

AOC, DOF, GOJ, and POQ are diameters.
AB̂C, DÊF, GĤJ, PM̂Q, PN̂Q and PR̂Q are all right angles (90°).
They are angles in a semicircle.

## Angle at the CENTRE is TWICE the angle at the CIRCUMFERENCE
e.g.

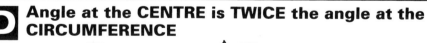

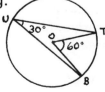 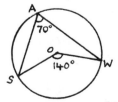 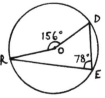

BÔT = 2 X BÛT   SÔW = 2 X SÂW   RÔD = 2 X RÊD

**a** Find the sizes of angles a, b, c, d, e, (not drawn to scale)

**b** Find the sizes of angles f, g, h, j and k. O is the centre. POQ, ROS, TOU, VOW and XOY are straight lines.

**c** Find the sizes of angles l, m, n, p, q (not drawn to scale). O is the centre of the circle.

**d** Find the sizes of angles r, s, t, u, v, w, x, y, z and a (not drawn to scale). O is the centre of the circle.

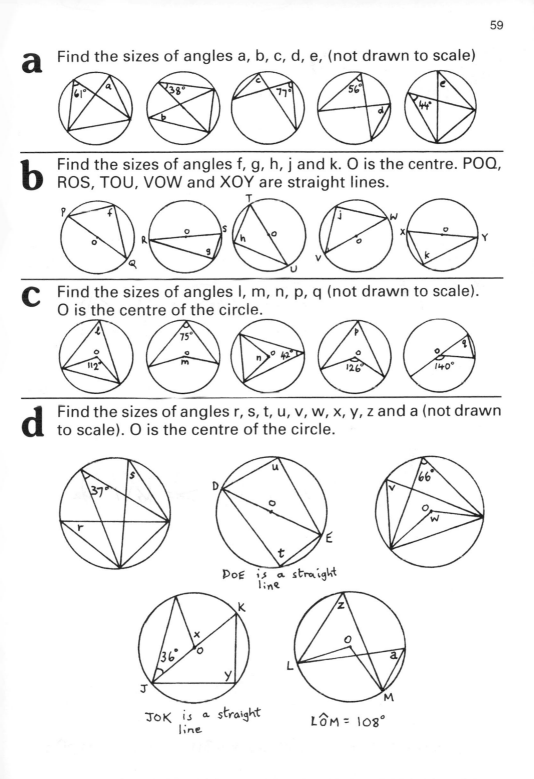

DOE is a straight line

JOK is a straight line

LÔM = 108°

# **A** CIRCLE (4)

## Cyclic quadrilateral

A cyclic quadrilateral is a quadrilateral whose four corners touch the circumference of the same circle. A cyclic quadrilateral fits exactly into a circle. The opposite angles of a cyclic quadrilateral add up to 180° (they are supplementary), e.g.

$$107° + 73° = 180°$$
$$96° + 84° = 180°$$

e.g. (2) Calculate angles a and b

$$a = 180° - 81° = 99°$$
$$b = 180° - 88° = 92°$$

## **B** Tangent

A tangent is a straight line, outside a circle, which just touches the circle. At the point where the tangent touches the circle, the tangent is at right angles (90°) to the radius.

This and other rules provide useful information
e.g.

O is the centre; PAQ and RBQ are tangents.
(1) $O\hat{A}P = O\hat{A}Q = O\hat{B}R = O\hat{B}Q = 90°$
(2) OA = OB
(3) AQ = BQ
(4) $A\hat{O}Q = B\hat{O}Q$ and $A\hat{Q}O = B\hat{Q}O$
(5) OQ bisects $A\hat{O}B$ and $A\hat{Q}B$
(6) △AOQ and △BOQ are congruent
(7) AQBO is a kite
(8) AB cuts OQ at right angles
(9) OQ bisects AB

REMEMBER (1) All radii of the same circle are of equal length
(2) The letter O in a circle diagram always means the centre.

61

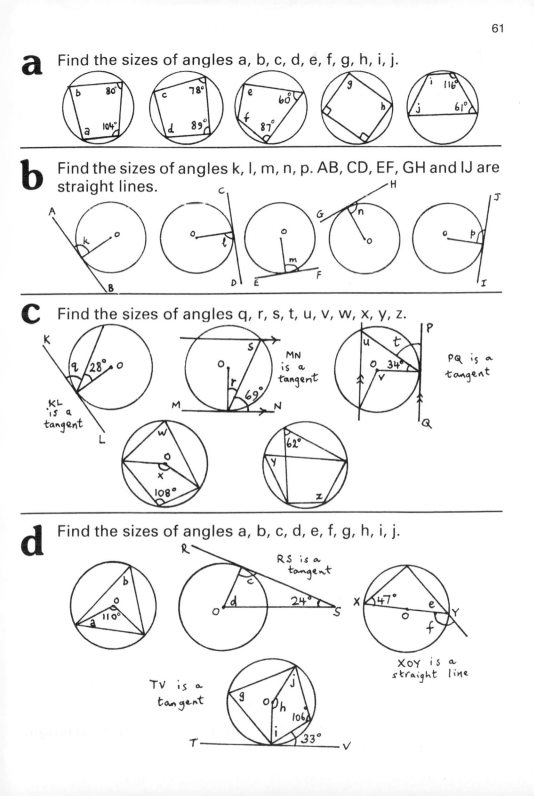

**a** Find the sizes of angles a, b, c, d, e, f, g, h, i, j.

**b** Find the sizes of angles k, l, m, n, p. AB, CD, EF, GH and IJ are straight lines.

**c** Find the sizes of angles q, r, s, t, u, v, w, x, y, z.

**d** Find the sizes of angles a, b, c, d, e, f, g, h, i, j.

# A 'ANGLE CHASING' WITH CIRCLES

## Some rules to remember

1) All radii of the same circle are equal in length.
2) Angles in the same segment are equal.
3) Angle in a semicircle is 90°.
4) Angle at the centre is twice the angle at the circumference.
5) Opposite angles of a cyclic quadrilateral are supplementary (add up to 180°)
6) Tangent is at right angles to the radius where it touches the circle.

It is a good idea also to revise other angle rules (see Maths for Practice & Revision, Book 4, page 66)

---

e.g. In this circle, find (i) DÂB, (ii) OÂB, (iii) DÂO, (iv) AÔE, (v) EF̂A, (vi) OÊF, (vii) CÂF, (viii) DÊF, giving brief reasons for your answers.

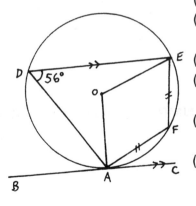

(i) DÂB = 56° (alternate with AD̂E)

(ii) OÂB = 90° (angle between tangent AB and radius OA)

(iii) DÂO = 34° (OÂB subtract DÂB)

(iv) AÔE = 112° (angle at centre is twice angle AD̂E)

(v) EF̂A = 124° (opposite to AD̂E in cyclic quad ADEF = 180°)

(vi) OÊF = 62° (OEFA is a kite with OÊF = OÂF. Angles in a quadrilateral = 360°)

(vii) CÂF = 28° (OÂC = 90°, angle between tangent BAC and radius OA)

(viii) DÊF = 84° (opposite to DÂF in cyclic quadrilateral ADEF, and DÂF = DÂO + OÂF = 34° + 62° = 96°)

---

**IF IN DIFFICULTY,** fill in **ANY** angles which you can work out. This may help you to find the one you want.

**a** In each diagram O is the centre of the circle. Give brief reasons for your answers.

1)

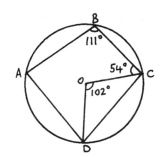

SRT is a straight line.
PQ = RQ
Find PÔR, OR̂P, QR̂P, PR̂S, OR̂Q and QR̂T.

2)

Find AD̂C, OĈD, BĈD, DÂB and AD̂O.

3)

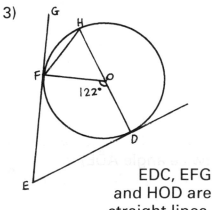

EDC, EFG and HOD are straight lines.
Find HÔF, DĤF, OF̂E, FÊD and HF̂E.

4)

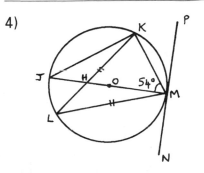

NMP and JOM are straight lines.
Find JK̂M, KĴM, KL̂M, KM̂P, LM̂K, LM̂J, LM̂N, KĤM and JĤL.

5)

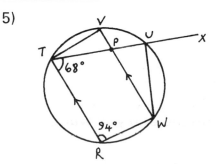

WV and RT are parallel.
RT̂U = 68°, TR̂W = 94°
Find TÛW, WÛX, TV̂W, TP̂W and PŴU.

# A SOLID FIGURES (1)

## Euler's Formula

The Swiss mathematician Leonhard Euler (pronounced oyler), who lived from 1707 until 1783, found that for many solids the **number of faces** added to the **number of vertices** (corners) was 2 more than the **number of edges,** or

$$faces + vertices = edges + 2$$
$$F + V = E + 2$$

e.g. A cuboid has 6 faces, 8 vertices and 12 edges.

This solid follows Euler's formula.

$$6 + 8 = 12 + 2$$

e.g. (2)

A solid made by sticking two congruent (identical) cones base to base has 2 faces, 2 vertices and 1 edge
$$2 + 2 \neq 1 + 2$$
Euler's formula does not apply to this solid.

e.g. (3) A solid which follows Euler's formula has 18 faces and 14 vertices. How many edges has it?

$$F + V = E + 2$$
$$18 + 14 = E + 2 \qquad E = 18 + 14 - 2 = 30$$

This solid has 30 edges

# B Volume of pyramid

Volume of pyramid = $\frac{1}{3}$ X area of base X height

e.g.

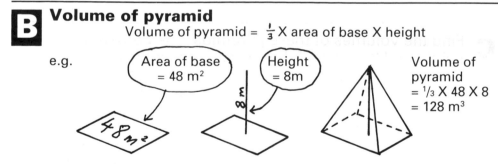

Volume of pyramid
= $\frac{1}{3}$ X 48 X 8
= 128 m³

NOTE. The height must always be the PERPENDICULAR HEIGHT from the base.

e.g. (2) Find the volume of a pyramid whose height is 10cm and whose base is a square with length 7.2 cm.

Area of base = 7.2 X 7.2 = 51.84 cm²
Volume of pyramid = $\frac{1}{3}$ X 51.84 X 10 = 172.8 cm³

REMEMBER. Volume is measured in CUBIC units, e.g. cubic metres (m³), cubic centimetres (cm³), etc.

**a** For each of these solids, list the number of faces, vertices and edges. Write down whether or not Euler's formula applies to the solid.

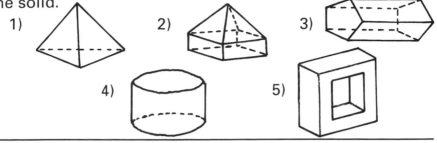

1)   2)   3)   4)   5)

**b** (All the solids in these questions follow Euler's formula)
1) A solid has 5 faces and 5 vertices. How many edges has it?
2) A dodecahedron has 12 faces and 30 edges. How many vertices has it?
3) A solid has 21 edges and 14 vertices. Calculate the number of faces it has.
4) An octahedron has 8 faces and 6 vertices. Find how many edges it has.
5) (a) A hendecagonal pyramid (whose base is an 11 sided figure) has 12 faces and 12 vertices. How many edges has it?
(b) If two congruent hendecagonal pyramids are stuck base to base to make a new solid, how many (i) faces, (ii) vertices, (iii) edges, has the new solid?

**c** Find the volumes of these pyramids. The perpendicular height and the area of the base are given for each.
1) Area of base 6m², perpendicular height 2m
2) Area of base 24cm², perpendicular height 7cm
3) Area of base 3m², perpendicular height 1m
4) Area of base 10m², perpendicular height 4.2m
5) Area of base 4x cm², perpendicular height 12y cm

**d** Find the volumes of these square pyramids. The perpendicular height and the length of the square base are given for each.
1) Length of base 9cm, perpendicular height 11cm
2) Length of base 0.6m, perpendicular height 0.5m
3) Length of base 2m, perpendicular height 1.5cm
4) Length of base 20cm, perpendicular height 30cm
5) Length of base 13cm, perpendicular height 21cm

# A SOLID FIGURES (2)

## Cylinders and Cones

A CYLINDER is a prism with a circular base.

<u>Surface area of cylinder</u>

Area of <u>curved surface</u> of cylinder

r = radius of base

h = height

Area of curved surface = 2 πrh

e.g. Find the area of the curved surface of a cylindrical tin which has radius 3cm and height 10cm (π = 3.14)

$$A = 2 \times 3.14 \times 3 \times 10$$
$$= \underline{188.4 \text{ cm}^2}$$

<u>Total surface area</u> of cylinder

= Area of curved surface (2πrh)

+ Area of base (πr²)

+ Area of top (πr²)

e.g. Calculate the total surface area of a cylinder with radius 4cm and height 6cm (π = 3.14).

$$A = (2\pi rh) + (\pi r^2) + (\pi r^2)$$
$$= 2\pi r(h + r)$$
$$= 2 \times 3.14 \times 4 \times 10 = \underline{251.2 \text{ cm}^2}$$

---

# B Volume of cylinder

Volume = πr²h

e.g. What is the volume (V) of a cylinder whose radius is 10cm and whose height is 32cm (π = 3.14) ?

$$V = 3.14 \times 10 \times 10 \times 32 = \underline{10048 \text{ cm}^3}$$

---

# C

A CONE is a pyramid with a circular base

<u>Volume of cone</u>

r = radius

h = height

Volume = $\frac{1}{3}\pi r^2 h$   or   $\frac{\pi r^2 h}{3}$

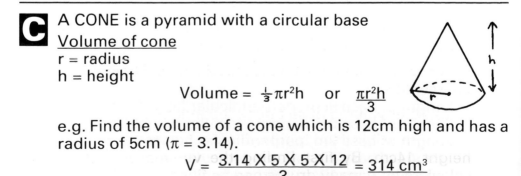

e.g. Find the volume of a cone which is 12cm high and has a radius of 5cm (π = 3.14).

$$V = \frac{3.14 \times 5 \times 5 \times 12}{3} = \underline{314 \text{ cm}^3}$$

Give answers to 2 significant figures

**a** (π = 3.14) Find the area of the curved surface of a cylinder with
1) radius 5cm, height 8cm
2) radius 2cm, height 6cm
3) radius 1m, height 1m
4) radius 6cm, height 20cm
5) radius 3m, height 10m
6) radius 10cm, height 50cm
7) radius ½m, height 2m
8) radius 0.7m, height 1.2m
9) radius 4cm, height 8cm
10) radius 11cm, height 30cm

**b** (π = 3.14) Find the total surface area of a cylinder with
1) radius 8cm, height 15cm
2) radius 5cm, height 5cm
3) radius 4cm, height 8cm
4) radius 1m, height 2m
5) radius 6cm, height 9cm

**c** Find the volume of a cylinder with
$(\pi = \frac{22}{7})$
1) radius 4cm, height 7cm
2) radius 10cm, height 35cm
3) radius 14cm, height 11cm
4) radius ½ m, height 1⅗ m
5) radius 63cm, height 60cm

(π = 3.14)
6) radius 10cm, height 20cm
7) radius 0.3m, height 1m
8) radius 4cm, height 8cm
9) diameter 18cm, height 18cm
10) radius 6cm, height 50cm

**d** (π = 3.14) Find the volume of a cone with
1) radius 6cm, height 6cm
2) radius 3cm, height 10cm
3) radius 0.5m, height 0.8m
4) radius 20cm, height 90cm
5) radius 15cm, height 24cm

**e** 1) What is the volume of a cylindrical biscuit tin with radius 13cm and height 12 cm?

2) A cylindrical cardboard tube for storing posters has a radius of 4cm and a height of 80cm. Find the area of cardboard used to make the tube (the area of the curved surface).

3) A firework in the shape of a cone has a radius of 5cm and is 10cm high. Find its volume.

4) An unopened cylindrical baked-bean can has a height of 6cm and a radius of 4cm. What is the total surface area?

5) $(\pi = \frac{22}{7})$ A cylindrical bin, radius 28cm and height 60cm, is filled with salt.

(a) What volume of salt does it contain?

(b) The salt is used to fill cylindrical drums of radius 4cm, height 14cm. By first finding the volume of each drum, calculate how many drums can be filled.

# SOME EXTRA QUESTIONS ( $\pi = 3.14$ )

1) (a) Multiply out $(2x + 5)(x + 4)$
   (b) Multiply out $(x - 9)(x + 9)$

2) Calculate the lengths of c and d (3 sig. figs.)

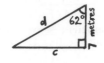

3) Solve these simultaneous equations $\quad 3x - y = 20$
   $\qquad\qquad\qquad\qquad\qquad\qquad\qquad 5x + y = 28$

4) (a) Find the square root of 3200 (3 sig. figs.)
   (b) Find the value of $\sqrt{0.074}$ (3 sig. figs.)

5) In the winter the owner of a house used 230 units of gas, 2050 units of electricity and 201 telephone units. In the spring he used 175 units of gas, 1640 electricity and 190 telephone. (a) Write these figures as a 3 X 2 matrix F. (b) Unit costs are: gas 40p per unit, electricity 6p, telephone 5p. Write these as a 1 X 3 matrix E. (c) Multiply EF and say what information this answer gives.

6) The longest side of a right-angled triangle is 61 cm long. One of the other sides is 60cm long. What is the length of the third side?

7) Using the table on page 72, or an electronic calculator, find the values of (a) sin 28°, (b) cos 61°, (c) 3 tan 40° (2 dec. places)

8) (i) Find (a) the median, (b) the range of

   $$60 \quad 64 \quad 63 \quad 68 \quad 71 \quad 58 \quad 67 \quad 70 \quad 58 \quad 73 \quad 68 \quad 59 \quad 69$$

   (ii) Find the mode in this group of letters

   $$P, \ E, \ A, \ R, \ T, \ R, \ E, \ E, \ C, \ O, \ T, \ T, \ A, \ G, \ E$$

9) An unopened cylindrical can has radius 6cm, height 17cm. Calculate (a) the area of its curved surface, (b) its total surface area, including top and bottom. (2 sig. figs.)

10) 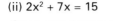 Write out Euler's formula and show how the formula applies to a triangular prism (shown in the diagram)

11) (a) $\begin{pmatrix} 3 & 2 \\ 1 & -2 \end{pmatrix} + \begin{pmatrix} -4 & 5 \\ 2 & -1 \end{pmatrix} + \begin{pmatrix} 2 & -3 \\ 4 & 0 \end{pmatrix}$

    (b) $4\begin{pmatrix} 1 & 2 \\ 0 & 4 \end{pmatrix} - \begin{pmatrix} 4 & -2 \\ 5 & 7 \end{pmatrix}$

12) Find the sizes of angles a and b

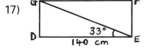

13) Add the vectors $\overrightarrow{RT} \begin{pmatrix} 3 \\ 2 \end{pmatrix}$ and $\overrightarrow{TZ} \begin{pmatrix} -5 \\ 3 \end{pmatrix}$. Write your answer as a column vector $\overrightarrow{RZ}$ and draw a diagram to represent the three vectors.

14) (a) Factorise into two brackets $x^2 + 9x + 18$
    (b) Factorise $3x^2 - 18x + 24$

15) (a) Find the circumference of a circle with radius 11cm (2 sig. figs.)
    (b) What is the perimeter of a semicircle with radius 6m (2 sig. figs.)?

16) Solve these quadratic equations by factorising into two brackets
    (i) $x^2 - 10x - 24 = 0$
    (ii) $2x^2 + 7x = 15$

17) The diagram shows a rectangular table top with DE=140cm and DÊG = 33°.

    Calculate, to the nearest centimetre, the perimeter of the table top.

18) Find the values of x and y if $\begin{pmatrix} 8 & x \\ 2y & 3 \end{pmatrix}\begin{pmatrix} 2 \\ 5 \end{pmatrix} = \begin{pmatrix} 6 \\ 11 \end{pmatrix}$

19) Five pencils and two rulers cost £1.03 altogether; three pencils and four rulers cost £1.29 altogether. Working in pence, use simultaneous equations to find the cost of (a) a pencil, (b) a ruler.

20) 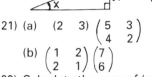 Work out the sine of angle x and, from your answer, write down the size of angle x (to the nearest degree).

21) (a) $(2 \quad 3)\begin{pmatrix} 5 & 3 \\ 4 & 2 \end{pmatrix}$

(b) $\begin{pmatrix} 1 & 2 \\ 2 & 1 \end{pmatrix}\begin{pmatrix} 7 \\ 6 \end{pmatrix}$

22) Calculate the area of (a) a circle with radius 6.5cm (2 sig. figs.)
(b) a semicircle with diameter 8cm (2 sig. figs.)

23) Find the possible values of x in each equation
(i) $(x - 2)(x - 5) = 0$ (ii) $(2x - 4)(x + 9) = 0$

24) Vector $a = \begin{pmatrix} 2 \\ 1 \end{pmatrix}$, $b = \begin{pmatrix} -3 \\ 2 \end{pmatrix}$. Write as column vectors (i) $4a - b$
(ii) $3b + 2a$

25) (i) Multiply $\begin{pmatrix} 2 \\ 3 \\ 4 \end{pmatrix}(5)$

(ii) Premultiply $(1 \quad 3 \quad 7)$ by $\begin{pmatrix} 5 \\ 4 \end{pmatrix}$

26) 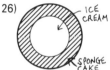 The diagram shows the circular cross-section (looking end on) of a cylindrical ice cream roll made of ice cream surrounded by sponge cake. The outer radius is 3.6cm and the inner radius is 2.8cm. Find (a) the area of sponge cake, (b) the volume of sponge cake if the roll is 11cm long. (2 sig. figs.)

27) (a) Multiply out $3(a + 2)(a - 3)$
(b) Multiply out $(x - 13)^2$

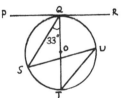

28) Find the size of (i) $R\hat{Q}O$, (ii) $P\hat{Q}S$, (iii) $S\hat{U}T$.
(PQR and QOT are straight lines)

29) To measure the height of the top of St Dominic's church spire, Toby stands 150m away and points his clinometer at the top of the spire. The clinometer records 21°. How high is the top of the spire?

30) Find the values of x and y if $3x + 2y = 18$ and $4x - 5y = 1$

31) Work out (a) the determinant, (b) the inverse of $\begin{pmatrix} 5 & 3 \\ 6 & 4 \end{pmatrix}$

32) Find (a) the mean, (b) the mode, (c) the median of this group of numbers
8 5 6 2 7 1 6 5 3 6
3 1 4 5 9 6 4 3 9 2

33) By using the formula on page 38 $\boxed{C}$ solve this quadratic equation correct to 2 decimal places: $3x^2 - 8x + 2 = 0$

34) (a) On squared paper, plot points (–1, 3), (–1, 5), (–2, 3) and join them to form a triangle. (b) Write the coordinates as a 2 X 3 matrix and premultiply by $\begin{pmatrix} 0 & 1 \\ -1 & 0 \end{pmatrix}$.

(c) Plot the points of the triangle given by the answer to (b) and describe fully what sort of transformation it is.

35) Twelve similar counters numbered ① ② ③ ④ ⑤ ⑥ ⑦ ⑧ ⑨ ⑩ ⑪ ⑫ are put in a bag and mixed up. Find the probability that a counter picked out of the bag will show
(a) an even number, (b) the number 13, (c) a prime number.

36) (i) Factorise $25x^2 - 36$
(ii) Factorise $hm - kn - hn + km$

37) A certain solid figure which follows Euler's formula has 14 vertices and 9 faces. How many edges has it?

38) The drive of a house is a steady slope of 16 metres from the road up to the front door. The drive makes an angle of 10° with the horizontal. How much higher than the road is the front door? Give answer to 2 significant figures.

39) Vector $a=\binom{-1}{1}$, $b=\binom{3}{2}$. $\overrightarrow{OK} = 3a$, $\overrightarrow{ON} = 2b$. (i) Draw $\overrightarrow{OK}$, $\overrightarrow{ON}$ and $\overrightarrow{NK}$. (ii) Write $\overrightarrow{NK}$ as a column vector and also in terms of a and b.

40) By drawing graphs, solve the simultaneous equations
$y = 3x - 2$ and $y = \frac{1}{2}x + 3$

41) Find the volume of (a) a pyramid with height 14cm and area of base 144 cm² (b) a cone with height 9cm and radius 4cm. (2 sig. figs.)

42) Multiply these matrices $\begin{pmatrix} 5 & 3 \\ 1 & -2 \end{pmatrix}\begin{pmatrix} 0 & 1 & -2 \\ -1 & 3 & 4 \end{pmatrix}$

43) There are 9 blue buttons, 6 red buttons and 21 white buttons in a box. (a) If I choose a button without looking, what is the probability that it will be blue? (b) If the button I have chosen is indeed blue and I leave it out of the box, what is the probability of choosing a white button if I dip into the box again?

44) Calculate the magnitude of vector $\binom{-5}{3}$. Give your answer to 3 significant figures.

45)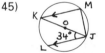
KOJ is a straight line; KM and LJ are parallel.
Find the sizes of (i) JK̂M, (ii) KM̂J, (iii) MĴK

46) Two boats 'Anna' and 'Billy' are heading for a port. 'Anna' is 2km due west of 'Billy' and 'Billy' is due south of the port. If 'Anna' sails on a bearing of 033° how far must she go to reach the port (2 sig. figs.)?

47) (a) Write these simultaneous equations in matrix form, and
(b) solve for x and y        $4x + 3y = 1$
$x + 2y = 4$

48) Sally is flying a kite on a string 240m long. The string makes an angle of 63° with the ground. What is the vertical height of the kite above the ground? (2 sig. figs.)

49) Clare told Adrian she had thought of a number, squared it, and then added the original number, making the final answer 30. Adrian guessed she had thought of 5 but he was wrong. What was Clare's original number?

50) A = 1, B = 2, C = 3, D = 4, E = 5, F = 6, G = 7. Carol uses the matrix
$\begin{pmatrix} 2 & -3 \\ -3 & 5 \end{pmatrix}$ to decode the message $\begin{pmatrix} 25 & 26 & 41 \\ 16 & 17 & 26 \end{pmatrix}$. What was the original
message?

# SQUARE ROOTS

| SQUARE ROOTS OF NUMBERS from 1.0 to 10.0 (3 sig. figs.) | | | |
| --- | --- | --- | --- |
| Number n | Square Root √n | Number n | Square Root √n |
| | | 5.1 | 2.26 |
| | | 5.2 | 2.28 |
| | | 5.3 | 2.30 |
| | | 5.4 | 2.32 |
| | | 5.5 | 2.35 |
| | | 5.6 | 2.37 |
| | | 5.7 | 2.39 |
| | | 5.8 | 2.41 |
| | | 5.9 | 2.43 |
| **1.0** | **1.00** | 6.0 | 2.45 |
| 1.1 | 1.05 | 6.1 | 2.47 |
| 1.2 | 1.10 | 6.2 | 2.49 |
| 1.3 | 1.14 | 6.3 | 2.51 |
| 1.4 | 1.18 | 6.4 | 2.53 |
| 1.5 | 1.22 | 6.5 | 2.55 |
| 1.6 | 1.26 | 6.6 | 2.57 |
| 1.7 | 1.30 | 6.7 | 2.59 |
| 1.8 | 1.34 | 6.8 | 2.61 |
| 1.9 | 1.38 | 6.9 | 2.63 |
| 2.0 | 1.41 | 7.0 | 2.65 |
| 2.1 | 1.45 | 7.1 | 2.66 |
| 2.2 | 1.48 | 7.2 | 2.68 |
| 2.3 | 1.52 | 7.3 | 2.70 |
| 2.4 | 1.55 | 7.4 | 2.72 |
| 2.5 | 1.58 | 7.5 | 2.74 |
| 2.6 | 1.61 | 7.6 | 2.76 |
| 2.7 | 1.64 | 7.7 | 2.77 |
| 2.8 | 1.67 | 7.8 | 2.79 |
| 2.9 | 1.70 | 7.9 | 2.81 |
| 3.0 | 1.73 | 8.0 | 2.83 |
| 3.1 | 1.76 | 8.1 | 2.85 |
| 3.2 | 1.79 | 8.2 | 2.86 |
| 3.3 | 1.82 | 8.3 | 2.88 |
| 3.4 | 1.84 | 8.4 | 2.90 |
| 3.5 | 1.87 | 8.5 | 2.92 |
| 3.6 | 1.90 | 8.6 | 2.93 |
| 3.7 | 1.92 | 8.7 | 2.95 |
| 3.8 | 1.95 | 8.8 | 2.97 |
| 3.9 | 1.97 | 8.9 | 2.98 |
| **4.0** | **2.00** | **9.0** | **3.00** |
| 4.1 | 2.02 | 9.1 | 3.02 |
| 4.2 | 2.05 | 9.2 | 3.03 |
| 4.3 | 2.07 | 9.3 | 3.05 |
| 4.4 | 2.10 | 9.4 | 3.07 |
| 4.5 | 2.12 | 9.5 | 3.08 |
| 4.6 | 2.14 | 9.6 | 3.10 |
| 4.7 | 2.17 | 9.7 | 3.11 |
| 4.8 | 2.19 | 9.8 | 3.13 |
| 4.9 | 2.21 | 9.9 | 3.15 |
| 5.0 | 2.24 | 10.0 | 3.16 |

| SQUARE ROOTS OF NUMBERS from 10 to 100 (3 sig. figs.) | | | |
| --- | --- | --- | --- |
| Number n | Square Root √n | Number n | Square Root √n |
| | | 51 | 7.14 |
| | | 52 | 7.21 |
| | | 53 | 7.28 |
| | | 54 | 7.35 |
| | | 55 | 7.42 |
| | | 56 | 7.48 |
| | | 57 | 7.55 |
| | | 58 | 7.62 |
| | | 59 | 7.68 |
| 10 | 3.16 | 60 | 7.75 |
| 11 | 3.32 | 61 | 7.81 |
| 12 | 3.46 | 62 | 7.87 |
| 13 | 3.61 | 63 | 7.94 |
| 14 | 3.74 | **64** | **8.00** |
| 15 | 3.87 | 65 | 8.06 |
| **16** | **4.00** | 66 | 8.12 |
| 17 | 4.12 | 67 | 8.19 |
| 18 | 4.24 | 68 | 8.25 |
| 19 | 4.36 | 69 | 8.31 |
| 20 | 4.47 | 70 | 8.37 |
| 21 | 4.58 | 71 | 8.43 |
| 22 | 4.69 | 72 | 8.49 |
| 23 | 4.80 | 73 | 8.54 |
| 24 | 4.90 | 74 | 8.60 |
| **25** | **5.00** | 75 | 8.66 |
| 26 | 5.10 | 76 | 8.72 |
| 27 | 5.20 | 77 | 8.77 |
| 28 | 5.29 | 78 | 8.83 |
| 29 | 5.39 | 79 | 8.89 |
| 30 | 5.48 | 80 | 8.94 |
| 31 | 5.57 | **81** | **9.00** |
| 32 | 5.66 | 82 | 9.06 |
| 33 | 5.74 | 83 | 9.11 |
| 34 | 5.83 | 84 | 9.17 |
| 35 | 5.92 | 85 | 9.22 |
| **36** | **6.00** | 86 | 9.27 |
| 37 | 6.08 | 87 | 9.33 |
| 38 | 6.16 | 88 | 9.38 |
| 39 | 6.24 | 89 | 9.43 |
| 40 | 6.32 | 90 | 9.49 |
| 41 | 6.40 | 91 | 9.54 |
| 42 | 6.48 | 92 | 9.59 |
| 43 | 6.56 | 93 | 9.64 |
| 44 | 6.63 | 94 | 9.70 |
| 45 | 6.71 | 95 | 9.75 |
| 46 | 6.78 | 96 | 9.80 |
| 47 | 6.86 | 97 | 9.85 |
| 48 | 6.93 | 98 | 9.90 |
| **49** | **7.00** | 99 | 9.95 |
| 50 | 7.07 | **100** | **10.0** |

PERFECT SQUARES are numbers whose square roots are exact integers (whole numbers).
Perfect squares and their square roots are shown in **BOLD PRINT.**

# SINES, COSINES AND TANGENTS (correct to 2 decimal places)

| ANGLE degrees | sin | cos | tan | ANGLE degrees | sin | cos | tan |
|---|---|---|---|---|---|---|---|
| 00 | 0 | 1.00 | 0 | | | | |
| 01 | 0.02 | 1.00 | 0.02 | 46 | 0.72 | 0.69 | 1.04 |
| 02 | 0.03 | 1.00 | 0.03 | 47 | 0.73 | 0.68 | 1.07 |
| 03 | 0.05 | 1.00 | 0.05 | 48 | 0.74 | 0.67 | 1.11 |
| 04 | 0.07 | 1.00 | 0.07 | 49 | 0.75 | 0.66 | 1.15 |
| 05 | 0.09 | 1.00 | 0.09 | 50 | 0.77 | 0.64 | 1.19 |
| 06 | 0.10 | 1.00 | 0.11 | 51 | 0.78 | 0.63 | 1.23 |
| 07 | 0.12 | 0.99 | 0.12 | 52 | 0.79 | 0.62 | 1.28 |
| 08 | 0.14 | 0.99 | 0.14 | 53 | 0.80 | 0.60 | 1.33 |
| 09 | 0.16 | 0.99 | 0.16 | 54 | 0.81 | 0.59 | 1.38 |
| 10 | 0.17 | 0.98 | 0.18 | 55 | 0.82 | 0.57 | 1.43 |
| 11 | 0.19 | 0.98 | 0.19 | 56 | 0.83 | 0.56 | 1.48 |
| 12 | 0.21 | 0.98 | 0.21 | 57 | 0.84 | 0.54 | 1.54 |
| 13 | 0.22 | 0.97 | 0.23 | 58 | 0.85 | 0.53 | 1.60 |
| 14 | 0.24 | 0.97 | 0.25 | 59 | 0.86 | 0.52 | 1.66 |
| 15 | 0.26 | 0.97 | 0.27 | 60 | 0.87 | 0.50 | 1.73 |
| 16 | 0.28 | 0.96 | 0.29 | 61 | 0.87 | 0.48 | 1.80 |
| 17 | 0.29 | 0.96 | 0.31 | 62 | 0.88 | 0.47 | 1.88 |
| 18 | 0.31 | 0.95 | 0.32 | 63 | 0.89 | 0.45 | 1.96 |
| 19 | 0.33 | 0.95 | 0.34 | 64 | 0.90 | 0.44 | 2.05 |
| 20 | 0.34 | 0.94 | 0.36 | 65 | 0.91 | 0.42 | 2.14 |
| 21 | 0.36 | 0.93 | 0.38 | 66 | 0.91 | 0.41 | 2.25 |
| 22 | 0.37 | 0.93 | 0.40 | 67 | 0.92 | 0.39 | 2.36 |
| 23 | 0.39 | 0.92 | 0.42 | 68 | 0.93 | 0.37 | 2.48 |
| 24 | 0.41 | 0.91 | 0.45 | 69 | 0.93 | 0.36 | 2.61 |
| 25 | 0.42 | 0.91 | 0.47 | 70 | 0.94 | 0.34 | 2.75 |
| 26 | 0.44 | 0.90 | 0.49 | 71 | 0.95 | 0.33 | 2.90 |
| 27 | 0.45 | 0.89 | 0.51 | 72 | 0.95 | 0.31 | 3.08 |
| 28 | 0.47 | 0.88 | 0.53 | 73 | 0.96 | 0.29 | 3.27 |
| 29 | 0.48 | 0.87 | 0.55 | 74 | 0.96 | 0.28 | 3.49 |
| 30 | 0.50 | 0.87 | 0.58 | 75 | 0.97 | 0.26 | 3.73 |
| 31 | 0.52 | 0.86 | 0.60 | 76 | 0.97 | 0.24 | 4.01 |
| 32 | 0.53 | 0.85 | 0.62 | 77 | 0.97 | 0.22 | 4.33 |
| 33 | 0.54 | 0.84 | 0.65 | 78 | 0.98 | 0.21 | 4.70 |
| 34 | 0.56 | 0.83 | 0.67 | 79 | 0.98 | 0.19 | 5.14 |
| 35 | 0.57 | 0.82 | 0.70 | 80 | 0.98 | 0.17 | 5.67 |
| 36 | 0.59 | 0.81 | 0.73 | 81 | 0.99 | 0.16 | 6.31 |
| 37 | 0.60 | 0.80 | 0.75 | 82 | 0.99 | 0.14 | 7.12 |
| 38 | 0.62 | 0.79 | 0.78 | 83 | 0.99 | 0.12 | 8.14 |
| 39 | 0.63 | 0.78 | 0.81 | 84 | 0.99 | 0.10 | 9.51 |
| 40 | 0.64 | 0.77 | 0.84 | 85 | 1.00 | 0.09 | 11.43 |
| 41 | 0.66 | 0.75 | 0.87 | 86 | 1.00 | 0.07 | 14.30 |
| 42 | 0.67 | 0.74 | 0.90 | 87 | 1.00 | 0.05 | 19.08 |
| 43 | 0.68 | 0.73 | 0.93 | 88 | 1.00 | 0.03 | 28.64 |
| 44 | 0.69 | 0.72 | 0.97 | 89 | 1.00 | 0.02 | 57.29 |
| 45 | 0.71 | 0.71 | 1.00 | 90 | 1.00 | 0 | ∞ |

∞  means 'infinity' (the highest imaginable number)